INDIANS

POCAHONTAS, *Seymour*
PONTIAC, *Peckham*
SACAGAWEA, *Seymour*
SEQUOYAH, *Snow*
SITTING BULL, *Stevenson*
SQUANTO, *Stevenson*
TECUMSEH, *Stevenson*

NAVAL HEROES

DAVID FARRAGUT, *Long*
GEORGE DEWEY, *Long*
JOHN PAUL JONES, *Snow*
MATTHEW CALBRAITH PERRY, *Scharbach*
OLIVER HAZARD PERRY, *Long*
RAPHAEL SEMMES, *Snow*
STEPHEN DECATUR, *Smith*

NOTED WIVES and MOTHERS

ABIGAIL ADAMS, *Wagoner*
DOLLY MADISON, *Monsell*
JESSIE FREMONT, *Wagoner*
MARTHA WASHINGTON, *Wagoner*
MARY TODD LINCOLN, *Wilkie*
NANCY HANKS, *Stevenson*
RACHEL JACKSON, *Govan*

BOOKER T. WASHINGTON, *Stevenson*
CLARA BARTON, *Stevenson*
DAN BEARD, *Mason*
FRANCES WILLARD, *Mason*
JANE ADDAMS, *Wagoner*
JOHN L. LEWIS, *Korson*
J. STERLING MORTON, *Moore*
JULIA WARD HOWE, *Wagoner*
JULIETTE LOW, *Higgins*
LILIUOKALANI, *Newman*
LUCRETIA MOTT, *Burnett*
MOLLY PITCHER, *Stevenson*
OLIVER WENDELL HOLMES, JR., *Dunham*
SUSAN ANTHONY, *Monsell*

SOLDIERS

ANTHONY WAYNE, *Stevenson*
BEDFORD FORREST, *Parks*
DAN MORGAN, *Bryant*
ETHAN ALLEN, *Winders*
FRANCIS MARION, *Steele*
ISRAEL PUTNAM, *Stevenson*

...enson

Ernie Pyle

Boy from Back Home

Illustrated by Isabel Dawson

Ernie Pyle

Boy from Back Home

By Ellen Wilson

THE **BOBBS-MERRILL** COMPANY, INC.
A SUBSIDIARY OF HOWARD W. SAMS & CO., INC.
Publishers • INDIANAPOLIS • NEW YORK

LIBRARY OF CONGRESS CATALOG CARD NUMBER: 62-12697

PRINTED IN THE UNITED STATES OF AMERICA

For Ernie's Aunt Mary
with affection and gratitude

Illustrations

Contents

Books by Ellen Wilson

ANNIE OAKLEY: LITTLE SURE SHOT
ERNIE PYLE: BOY FROM BACK HOME

★ Ernie Pyle

Boy from Back Home

U.S

Ernie Starts a Collection

A SMALL boy in overalls squatted beside a country road in Indiana. He was pretending he could write his name, "Ernest Pyle." With a short stick he made curlicues in the thick dust.

"There! That looks almost like real writing," he said to himself.

He hitched up one overalls strap that kept slipping. Then he looked again at the marks in the dust. The curlicues went round and round.

"I reckon nobody else would think it was writing, though. It looks more like bedsprings. I guess I'll have to wait till I go to school before I can learn to write the real way."

Ernie sighed. A whole year was a long time to wait to be six and go to school.

He stood up and erased all the marks with his bare toes. He brushed his shaggy hair out of his eyes. Then he took another long look down the dusty road.

"Where is that mailman?" he asked. "His horse and buggy ought to be down by the Baleses' house by now, but I don't see the buggy. I don't see anything. And there's nothing to do. I wish I had a brother to play with," he thought, "or even a sister."

Again Ernie looked down the road for his friend, the mailman. "Maybe he'll come quicker if I don't look," he decided.

Ernie took hold of the post that held up the big, shiny mailbox. He shut his eyes. Slowly he started swinging around the post. His thatch of gold-red hair just brushed the underside of the mailbox each time around.

He kept his eyes tight shut. Round and round he went. Faster and faster he swung. At last he let go. He was so dizzy he could not stand up straight. He wobbled a few steps. Then he sat down *ker-plop* in the thick grass.

He opened his eyes. His head was spinning. The world was spinning, too. How funny everything looked, going around in circles! The house, the fields, the road, and even the mailbox went whirling round him. Even the five maple trees by the drive seemed to sail through the air. Everything was swinging round and round his head. It didn't look like home at all. It looked like a strange and exciting place, far, far away, that he had never seen before.

Now everything began to slow down. Soon even the shiny mailbox settled into its proper place. And there by the mailbox was the mailman in his buggy.

"Hello there, young fellow," said the mailman.

"What did you think you were doing? Playing you were a merry-go-round?"

"I was waiting for you," Ernie said. He got unsteadily to his feet. "Any mail today?"

"Yes sirree, there's mail today. Here's the Dana *News* for Mr. William C. Pyle."

"That's my papa. You know him."

"Here's the Sears, Roebuck catalogue for Fall 1905, for Mrs. Maria Taylor Pyle."

"That's my mama. You know her."

"And here's a letter for Miss Mary Taylor."

"That's my auntie. You know her, too."

"Well, I guess that's all today."

"Oh!" said Ernie, taking the mail. He felt disappointed. "Isn't there anything for me?" He almost never got any mail, but he always asked anyhow.

"Wait a minute. Seems like there was something else. Yes, here's a picture post card addressed to:

Master Ernest Taylor Pyle
R.F.D.
Dana
Indiana

Anybody by that name live here?"

"That's me! You know that's me," Ernie cried excitedly.

He dropped the heavy catalogue and other mail on the grass. He stood on tiptoe and held out his hand for the card.

The mailman held it just out of reach. "Oh, are you Ernest Taylor Pyle?" he teased. "I thought you were just a merry-go-round."

"My picture card! Please give me my picture card," Ernie begged. He jumped up and down in his excitement.

"All right, here you are." With one hand the mailman gave a playful tug at Ernie's curly hair. With the other he handed down the bright-colored post card.

Ernie looked at the picture eagerly. He saw a slim white monument, stretching up into a bright blue sky. On the ground below were beautiful trees and smooth green grass. He turned the card over. On the back was real writing, not just curlicues. He wished he could read it.

A screen door slammed. "Ernest," his mother called from the porch, "hurry up with the mail."

Ernie picked up everything from the grass. It was hard to carry the heavy catalogue and run at the same time. When he reached the porch of the white farmhouse he was panting.

"Mama, Mama, guess what! There's a card for me. It's written just to me. Where is it from? What does it say? Read it quick."

"Just a minute, Ernest." His mother smiled down at him. She wiped her hands on her blue apron. Then she put on her glasses.

"That's a pretty picture, isn't it?" she said. Then she turned the card over and read:

> Dear Ernest, this is a picture of the Washington Monument in Washington, D.C. Tomorrow we are going to the White House. Someday you must come to our nation's capital. Maybe you'll even have a chance to shake hands with the President of the United States.
>
> Yours truly, Lucy Campbell

"Why," said Mama, "it's from Miss Campbell, your friend up the road. I didn't know she was going visiting that far away."

"Someday I will go to Washington, just as she says," Ernie said. "I'd like to see the President. But I won't shake hands with him."

"You won't!" cried Aunt Mary, who came out onto the porch just then. "Why won't you, Ernest? It would be a great honor."

"Because I wouldn't dare," Ernie said. "Not a famous man like him. I wouldn't know what to say." Ernie looked worried.

"Just let him do the talking." Mama laughed. "You wouldn't have to say much except maybe howdy-do."

"Oh, I couldn't!" Ernie protested. "But I'll climb clear up to the top of that monument someday, and I'll look out and see everything. Do you suppose I could see Dana from 'way up there, Aunt Mary?"

Aunt Mary laughed. "Well, I don't reckon you could see clear back to a little town like Dana even from atop that monument."

"Go call your papa now," Mama said. "Tell him dinner's ready."

During dinner Ernie could hardly keep his eyes off his post card. He propped it up against his glass of buttermilk. "It's the first card I ever got all to myself," he said blissfully. "Do you suppose I'll ever get another one?"

"Of course you will," Mama said.

Ernie had an idea. "Then I could start a collection, couldn't I? I could keep the cards in my shoe box."

"You can start a collection right now with this card," Aunt Mary said. "We'll give you any post cards that come for us, too, and it won't take so long to build your collection up."

Mama and Papa nodded.

"Meantime," Papa said, "how about coming out to watch me and the horses do the plowing this afternoon?"

"I will if I can bring my picture card along."

Mama and Aunt Mary laughed.

"You do enjoy that card, don't you, Ernest?" Aunt Mary said.

Papa laughed, too. "You'll never make a farmer that way," he said. "I never heard tell of a farmer who could plow and look at picture post cards at the same time."

Ernie Gets a Licking

Ernie walked back and forth, back and forth, the length of the field. In front of him Papa was holding on to the handles of the plow. Ahead were the two work horses, pulling the plow. Their heads nodded in the heat of the late-September sun.

Ernie was growing sleepy, too. He wiggled his bare toes in the fresh, soft furrows made by the plow. Papa said Ernie couldn't do any plowing himself until he was bigger. Now he could just watch and learn how Papa did it.

Ernie was already tired of walking and watching, however. By and by his father came to a weedy fence row at the edge of the field. Ernie saw some late red roses growing there.

"Mama would like some of those roses for her cut-glass vase," he thought. "So would Auntie. But they look prickly. I wish I had a knife."

"Papa," he called, "would you lend me your jackknife? I want to cut some roses to take back to the house."

Papa stopped the horses. He looked disgusted. "Who ever heard of a farmer stopping to cut roses?" Then he laughed. "Well, here you are," he said, and gave Ernie the knife. "Be sure to give it back to me. It's the best knife I have. Don't lose it now."

"I won't," Ernie promised.

He sat down in the tall grass and weeds by the fence row. He cut ten of the wild roses. The knife was a big help. Still, he got his thumb full of thorns. He stopped to pull them out. Then he started cutting roses again.

Suddenly a blue-racer snake came looping through the weeds. It was coming straight toward him. Ernie froze. The snake saw him and raised its blue-green head high in the air. It stopped for a moment, swaying back and forth. Then it started toward him again. Ernie screamed. He dropped the knife and ran as fast as he could.

Papa was at the other end of the field now. When Ernie saw him he remembered the knife. He didn't dare lose it, but he was afraid to go back. What if the snake was still there? Still, he knew he had to find that jackknife. He had promised Papa he wouldn't lose it.

Ernie took a deep breath and crept back to where he thought he had dropped the knife. He stepped carefully along one of the furrows and looked all around him. There it was! The shiny blade was sticking up from the freshly plowed ground just in front of him.

Ernie gave a long sigh of relief. He was glad it wasn't in the high weeds. He didn't think he could make himself walk into that overgrown patch. He shuddered. The blue racer was probably there right now, waiting for him.

He ran back across the field and gave the knife to Papa. "A snake!" he gasped. "There was a big blue racer coming right at me. I'm going home." And Ernie was off.

It was a long way to the house. Ernie ran fast. He wouldn't feel safe until he was inside. Mama would be there—and Auntie. He'd help them in the kitchen. No more plowing for him!

He climbed over the fence at the back of the house. Then he stopped short. The only way he could get to the back yard was through the old, deserted garden. He had forgotten that. It was full of high weeds. What if another snake was hiding there? What if a whole nest of blue racers was in those weeds?

"Mama," he shouted. "Mama, come get me!"

For a minute there was silence. Then he heard his mother's voice. "Why should I come get you? Come on by yourself."

"I can't. I can't. All these weeds!"

"Of course there are weeds. What's the matter with you? Are you hurt?"

"N-no." Ernie was crying now. "But I can't walk through the weeds by myself."

Ernie's mother came to the back door. "Don't be foolish, Ernest. A five-year-old boy afraid of a few weeds! What's got into you, anyhow?"

Ernie couldn't tell her. All he could say was, "Come get me. Please come get me." He said it over and over again between his sobs.

"Ernest Taylor Pyle, stop this nonsense! If you don't come through those weeds I'll whip you. Come on, now. I mean it."

Ernie put out one bare foot, but he couldn't take the first step. He began to cry harder.

His mother started toward him. She walked fast. Her skirts swished through the weeds. "Bringing me away from my pumpkin pies!" she said. "I've no time for such foolishness."

With one hand she caught Ernie's arm. Then she bent him over and spanked him with the other. She spanked him hard.

It was the first licking Ernie had ever had, but he didn't really mind. He even stopped crying. A licking wasn't nearly so bad as snakes.

His mother marched Ernie back into the house. She told him to go to his room and stay there till suppertime. He didn't mind that, either. There were no snakes in there. He took his picture post card out of his overalls pocket and set it up on the washstand to look at. It was a little crumpled. He would have to be careful or it would get all bent.

After supper Mama told Papa about Ernie. "I can't make head or tail of it," she said. "He carried on something terrible, and all about walking through a few weeds."

Then Papa told her about the snake and how brave Ernest was to go back and get the knife because he had promised not to lose it. "Didn't he tell you what he was doing with the knife?" he asked. He smiled and patted Ernie gently on the shoulder.

Mama shook her head.

"Why, he was cutting some wild roses. For you—for your cut-glass vase."

Mama looked at Ernie. She tried to smile, but she began to cry instead. Mama crying! Ernie didn't know grownups ever cried.

Later when he was in bed, Mama came in to tell him good night. She sat down in the rocker and talked to him. "I didn't understand, Ernest. You should have told me about the snake instead of making such a racket. When you're frightened of something, don't be afraid to say so. I wouldn't have given you that licking if I had known about the snake. I'm sorry."

"I'm sorry, too, Mama. I'm sorry I forgot to bring you the roses. I was in too much of a hurry, I guess."

After Mama went downstairs, Ernie lay awake for a while. "I remembered the knife for Papa, but I forgot the roses for Mama," he thought. "I wish I hadn't left them out in the field."

Just before he went to sleep, Ernie made a plan. It was a good plan. But to make it work he would have to get up early, and he would have to be a lot braver than he had been today.

Ernie's Plan

WHEN ERNIE opened his eyes the next morning he could tell that it was very early. The light outside his small windowpane was still pale gray. He turned over to go back to sleep. Then he remembered his plan.

Last night it had seemed like a wonderful idea, but this morning he wasn't so sure. He didn't want to think about it. He would just go to sleep again and forget it.

He was drifting off to sleep when he heard Mama's white rooster crow. It crowed loud and long. Soon the whole family would be getting up. It wouldn't be long till his mother would be starting breakfast. At the thought of Mama, Ernie sat up in bed. He just had to try his plan. Maybe he couldn't do it, but he'd try, anyway.

His feet hit the floor. Ernie dressed quickly. Once he looked at his high black shoes, standing neatly side by side under the bed. If he could wear them, it would help a lot. But in warm weather he had to save his shoes. They were for wearing into Dana on Saturday nights. They were for wearing to church on Sundays.

Barefooted, Ernie crept down the steep stairway. He stepped carefully over the one board that always creaked. In the kitchen he stopped. He pulled one of the short paring knives from the knife rack. Quietly he opened the back door and stepped outside.

Streaks of red were beginning to show in the sky. Birds called sleepily from the maple trees. It was going to be a beautiful morning, but Ernie did not notice that. All he saw were the tall weeds between him and the fence. They were the same old weeds he would not go through yesterday. Fear began to sweep over him again. His stomach felt queer. He'd better go right now before he lost his courage.

Ernie took a deep breath. Then he hurried across the yard and plunged into the patch of high weeds. He made himself walk right through them. He walked fast, but he did not run. When he got to the fence he climbed over it. Then he started across the fields.

He slowed down when he came to the field where he had seen the snake yesterday. He looked for the roses he had cut. Yes, they were still there, scattered on the ground, but they were all dead. He would have to cut fresh ones for Mama. It was a good thing he had brought the kitchen knife.

Ernie took another deep breath. His stomach was feeling funny again, but he started to cut roses from the hedgerow. He could not help thinking about the snake—the blue racer. Once he thought he heard a rustling noise in the weeds, but he kept on cutting. He did not stop when the thorns pricked him. He did not stop until he had a dozen bright red blossoms. The roses in his hand were all wet with dew. He cut two more, for good measure. Now he could start home.

For the first time he heard the meadow larks singing. He saw the sun, red above the horizon. When he got to the high weeds by the back yard his stomach still felt a little queer. But he made his feet keep going.

In the kitchen Aunt Mary and Papa were sitting down to breakfast. Mama was busy at the stove. When Ernie held out his bunch of flowers to her, she did not say anything. She just gave him a big hug. Then she took the roses and filled her cut-glass vase with water from the pump.

"Well, well, what's all this?" Papa asked. "Does this mean you aren't afraid of snakes any more, Ernest?"

Ernie thought a minute. "I guess I still am afraid. My stomach still gets scared."

Mama smiled. "But your feet don't, and that's what counts. You'll be all right as long as you make your feet keep going."

Ernie grinned. Suddenly he was very happy. He was hungry, too.

Mama put the vase of roses in the middle of the table beside the plate of hot biscuits. "Never thought we'd be fixing a bunch of flowers for breakfast," she said. "But then, this is a right special occasion."

SATURDAY NIGHT IN DANA

Ernie thought going into Dana that night was a special occasion, too. He always liked Saturday nights in Dana even though he had to get all dressed up. But it was special this time because Papa gave him fifty cents to spend.

"Spend it on anything you want," Papa said.

Ernie had never had a whole half dollar before. He usually had just a nickel to spend. Almost always he spent it on licorice whips.

Papa let Ernie hold the reins as they drove the surrey into Dana. They stopped in the middle of town. Horses and buggies lined both sides of Main Street. Ernie jumped down from the surrey. He tied the horse to one of the hitching posts. Then the shopping began.

Mama and Aunt Mary bought groceries. Papa got some feed for the hens. Ernie was allowed to choose some gingham for a new shirt. He picked out a bright red plaid.

He kept feeling in the pocket of his knickers to make sure his fifty-cent piece was still there. He wasn't going to spend it until they went to

Uncle John's store. Ernie thought that was the best store in town.

Now and then the Pyles would stop and talk to their friends who were in from the country too. "People are always sociable on Saturday nights," Ernie thought.

He didn't say much, himself, but he liked to listen to the grownups talk and laugh.

At last the Pyles went in to visit with Uncle John. Over his store was a sign: JOHN TAYLOR, TOYS AND SUNDRIES.

Ernie often wondered what sundries were. Once when he had asked Uncle John, his uncle had just laughed and said, "I reckon sundries means everything in the store that isn't toys."

Tonight Ernie walked up and down the long aisle between the two counters. Both counters were piled high with all kinds of things: tops and string and rubber balls and roller skates and dolls. There was a special candy counter. Ernie leaned against that for a long time. His mouth watered, but he did not buy any licorice whips. Next he looked at some books. They had paper covers with exciting pictures on the front. Ernie wished he could read.

Suddenly he caught sight of a special kind of book. It had a colored cover made of padded leather. Ernie like the feel of the leather. He liked the shiny gold letters on the outside. When he opened it to look inside, he could see it was not a storybook. The pages were plain. There was no printing on them. They had funny little slits cut into them. What could they be?

When Uncle John came by, Ernie stopped him. "What do these gold letters say? What kind of book is this?"

Uncle John bent down and explained, "It's called *My Post Card Collection*. It's an album to keep picture cards in. You stick the corners of the cards in these little slits. See? That way you can keep cards nice and straight without bending or breaking them."

"Oh!" Ernie's eyes sparkled. "That's much better than an old shoe box. How much is it, Uncle John?"

"Seventy-five cents," Uncle John said.

"Oh!" said Ernie again. He felt in his knickers pocket. The fifty-cent piece was still there, all right, but it wouldn't be enough. "I know seventy-five cents is more than fifty, but how much more?"

"Twenty-five cents more—a quarter," said Uncle John. "What's on your mind, Ernest? Do you want this album? Do you have a card collection?"

"Yes, I've got one card already. It's a picture of the Washington Monument. But I've got only fifty cents."

"Hmm," said his Uncle John with a frown. "Wouldn't you like a toy just as well? We've got some right nice toys for less than fifty cents. Then you'd have some money left over for candy, too."

Ernie swallowed. "No, I don't want a toy or candy this time. I want a sundry."

Uncle John laughed. "This particular sundry, eh? Well, why don't you ask your papa for a quarter, Ernest?"

Ernie looked quickly at Papa. He was busy talking to Mr. Bales at the other end of the store.

"I guess I'd better not ask him for any more money. He gave me fifty cents today. I usually get only a nickel for Saturday night."

"How come you have so much money today? Is it your birthday?"

"Oh, no," said Ernie. "My birthday is over. It was in August. I got the fifty cents because——" He hesitated. He wanted to tell Uncle John all about going through the weeds this morning, but he decided it might sound like bragging. Well—just because," Ernie finished lamely.

A customer called to Uncle John. Ernie was left alone with the album. He ran his finger over the sparkling gold letters and then looked inside. He could just see how nice his picture card would look there. He would tuck the corners into the slits on the very first page. Then the card would be all smooth and straight.

"Come along, Ernest. It's time to go home," said Papa.

Ernie tried to say something about the album, but Papa, Aunt Mary, and Mama were already going out the door. It was too late now.

On the way home Ernie was very quiet.

Aunt Mary asked him, "What did you get with your half dollar?"

"Nothing," Ernie said. "Not even candy."

Aunt Mary was surprised. "Did you see anything you wanted?"

CARD

"Yes, but——" Ernie stopped.

Then Ernie told them all about the album with the gold letters. He could hardly keep his voice steady when he said, "But it cost seventy-five cents, and I didn't have that much."

"Well," Papa said cheerfully, "you've got a good start with that fifty cents of yours. Why don't you begin saving up your nickels? Then you'll have enough to buy the album before too many Saturday nights go by."

"How many Saturday nights?" asked Ernie.

"Only five."

Ernie sighed. Five Saturday nights seemed a long time to wait.

It was such a long time that Ernie got discouraged. On the third Saturday night he spent one of his precious nickels. Mariam Bales, a little neighbor girl, begged him to. "She wanted some licorice whips an awful lot," Ernie explained to his family. "This kind, with pink sugar polka dots." He took another big bite. "Besides," he confided, "I kind of wanted some myself."

After that he decided to stay away from the candy counter. He decided to stay away from Mariam, too. And when he went home from Uncle John's on the sixth Saturday night, he had the red-leather album with him. He had bought and paid for it with his own money.

At home he put his Washington Monument card in the slits on the first page. It looked fine. "Just like a picture in a frame," Ernie said. He showed it proudly to the family. He ran his finger over the shiny gold letters on the album cover. "Now it really is *My Post Card Collection*, the way it says."

The Right Person to Belong To

IT WAS Christmastime before Ernie got another card to put in his album. Great-aunt Nancy Miller sent it from Chicago. This card had a picture of Santa Claus on it. His beard was made of real cotton, white and fluffy. When Ernie blew on it the beard fluttered up and down. He liked it.

"I can't play with post cards all the time, though. What can I do now?" he asked Mama one day.

Mama answered, "There's always plenty to do. The wood box is empty again. How about filling it?"

Papa said, "When you've done that, come help me in the barn. I'm mending harness today."

"All right," Ernie said, "but that's work. I wish I had someone to play with."

Next morning when Ernie came into the kitchen, he rubbed the sleep out of his eyes. "Chores wouldn't be so bad if I only had a dog to go the rounds with me," he thought. But he didn't say anything about that. He just grumbled a little about having to get up so early.

"If we didn't get up before the sun," Papa said, "we wouldn't get all the work done. The animals wake up early. The horses and cows and chickens have to be watered and fed. The hogs, too. You know that."

Yes, Ernie knew all that. But sometimes it seemed to him that he and Papa were always feeding the animals.

Then he grinned as he sat down to breakfast. Mama and Aunt Mary were always feeding

Papa and him, too. That was all right with Ernie. He was sure that nobody in the world made such good buckwheat cakes as Mama.

Ernie held a big pitcher over his first plateful of pancakes. Finally, the thick brown sorghum molasses came out. He poured it round and round in circles. When Mama gave him his next plateful, he poured the sorghum all in one spot. It made a shiny puddle.

"Since you eat so many buckwheat cakes and so much molasses every morning, I should think you'd fatten up a little." His mother laughed. "You don't, though. You stay skinny as a rail."

She gave him an anxious pat on the head. "Now if the rest of you would only grow as fast as this red mop of yours! I declare, I never saw such shaggy hair."

Papa put on his thick sweater and started out the back door. "Come along now, Ernest. Time you were feeding Mama's chickens."

Ernie licked the last dribble of molasses off his sticky fingers. He took his stocking cap and heavy sweater down from the hook on the kitchen door and put them on.

In the chicken house the hens clucked all round him. He shooed them away, so he could fill up their watering pans. Then he gave them their feed.

Ernie liked the hens. "They're sort of silly, though," he thought. "Always cackling and clucking and getting in one another's way. You can't tell them anything—not the way you can a dog. I wish old Rip was still around."

Rip was Papa's sheep dog who had died of old age. Papa said they'd get a new dog someday. "But," he always added, "he will have to be smart and do his share of the work. We can't have a dog that doesn't earn his keep."

Ernie went on up the hill to the barn. Horses and cows were better than chickens. Especially horses. Papa always let Ernie hold the reins now when they drove the surrey into Dana, and Auntie let him ride her horse, Old Kate, sometimes. Old Kate was so gentle Ernie knew he couldn't fall off her even if he tried. Still, he wished he had a horse. Or a dog. Or a pet of some kind, all his own.

"Why don't you try milking again this morning?" Papa asked. "Try Bessie. I haven't milked her yet. Now remember what I've told you. Come at her from her right-hand side."

"Why don't you ever milk from the left?" Ernie asked.

"I don't know why. You just don't, that's all. Now start with your right hand. Not your left—your right."

"But I always use my left hand. For everything," Ernie protested.

"Well, all right. Try it that way."

Papa told Ernie just what to do. Ernie tried.

Nothing happened. He tried again. This time a small trickle of milk went up his sleeve. It startled him so much he let go.

"Not that way. Now watch." Papa got a fine, steady stream of milk. "See You've got to make it sing into the pail."

Ernie tried again. He got a stream, all right, but this time it went on his overalls.

Papa laughed. "I guess you'd better stick to the chickens for a while longer. Now go down to the house and get Mama to wipe you off."

"Cows aren't any fun at all," Ernie thought, as he ran down the hill.

In the kitchen sat Will Bales, an older boy. He was Mariam's cousin. There were two Bales families in the neighborhood.

"Hello, Shag," Will said.

"Why do you always call me that?" Ernie asked. "The family doesn't."

"Because your head is so shaggy, that's why."

Ernie didn't mind. He liked Will, and Shag was all right for a nickname. Suddenly something caught his eye, something all curled up on the rag rug by the wood stove.

"A dog!" He ran over to pet it. "A shepherd dog! Who does it belong to?"

"Well now, I don't rightly know," Will said. "I found him wandering around our place last night. He was tuckered out. Hungry, too. He's only half grown. I reckon maybe he's looking for someone to belong to."

"Oh! May I keep him?" Ernie's gray eyes were eager as he looked from Mama to Aunt Mary. "May I?"

"If Papa says yes," Mama said.

"I reckon so," said Aunt Mary.

"Oh!" Ernie said. He stroked the dog's thick coat. "Papa will say yes. He says I can have a dog if he's smart. Anybody can see this is a smart dog."

At this the dog thumped his plume of a tail on the rug. Everybody laughed.

"What are you going to call him?" Will asked.

"He has a nice shaggy coat. How about 'Shag'?" suggested Aunt Mary.

"No," Will objected. "You've already got one Shag in the family."

"I know," Ernie said quickly. "He's a shepherd dog, so his name ought to be 'Shep.' Isn't that your name, Shep?"

This time the dog thumped his tail rapidly. He got up and stuck his cold nose into Ernie's hand.

"See?" Ernie was delighted. "He knows his name, and he knows he's found the right person to belong to."

A BOY'S BEST FRIEND

All that summer Shep helped on the farm. He helped Papa bring in the cows for milking. He helped Ernie keep the chickens from straying too far away.

"He's a right good watchdog, too," Aunt Mary said. "This morning he barked so hard he scared away that tramp who was pestering us."

Ernie was proud of Shep, but he had felt sorry for the tramp, too. Maybe tramps were pests to the grownups. Just the same, Ernie liked them. He decided the next time one came around he'd hold on to Shep's collar. Then the tramp would not be scared. This morning Shep had chased the tramp clear off the place.

Shep was a big help to everybody in the family. But there was no doubt about it; he was Ernie's dog. The two went everywhere together. With Shep along, Ernie's stomach no longer felt funny when he walked through the high weeds. The day Shep killed a snake, Ernie decided Shep was the best friend a boy could have.

"I declare," Mama said, "that dog can do everything but read and write."

"Well, I can't read or write, either," Ernie said. "If they'd only let Shep start to school with me next week, I bet we could learn together."

The Indian Mound

AFTER ERNIE'S first day at school Mama and Aunt Mary were full of questions. Ernie tried to answer them while he ate some cookies and drank a glass of milk.

"I didn't learn how to write. Teacher says it takes longer than one day." He looked disappointed. "Mariam Bales was there. She's smart. She knew how to write before she even went to school. We played during lunch hour. I pulled her pigtails. She squealed."

"Oh, Ernest," Mama said, "you mustn't pull girls' braids!"

"It didn't really hurt. She was just pretending.

Anyhow, I have another friend. His name is Thad Hooker. He's just moved here. He's bigger'n me but he's nice. He has a pony. He wants me to come over this afternoon. Can I go?" Ernie looked eagerly at his mother. "Can I, Mama, please?"

"Why, yes, I guess so. Be back in time to feed the chickens, remember."

"Come on, Shep, let's go! A boy with a pony is more fun than a girl, even if she can write and has braids."

After that first afternoon with Thad, Ernie never had to ask, "What can I do now?" There was always plenty to do. There was always Thad to play with, and to work with, too. They helped each other with chores so they could get through them faster.

After school Ernie could go over to Thad's house. Or Thad would come over to the Pyle house. Saturdays were best because Thad could stay all day. Mama always put on an extra plate at dinnertime.

"I declare," she would say, smiling at the two boys, "I feel we have twins in the family."

Ernie wondered how he had ever got along without Thad. Thad was always ready for anything, and he thought Ernie had good ideas about games to play.

On nice days one of the boys' favorite spots was the Indian mound. This was another big hill near the house. It was covered with bushes and trees. When summer came, Ernie and Thad played Indians on the mound. Sometimes they dug for Indian treasure.

"There are bound to be some arrowheads," Ernie said.

"Or even tomahawks," Thad added.

By the time Ernie was almost eight, the boys had dug dozens of holes, but so far they had not found a single thing.

One day Ernie was just about to give up. Thad had more patience, but he agreed that digging was hot work. It was very warm. Ernie threw down his spade. He wiped the sweat from his face.

"Why don't we go fishing down in Mr. Webster's crick?" he asked. "We can catch catfish easier than we can find any old arrowheads."

"In a minute," Thad said. He drove his spade in for one last, good dig. His spade hit something hard. It made a sharp, ringing sound.

Excitedly the boys scraped the dirt off it. Shep helped. He barked wildly and made the earth fly.

"Golly Ned! I do believe we've got something at last! And not just a rock, either," Thad said.

The boys tugged and pulled. At last they got it out. It was a perfect tomahawk blade. Thad turned it over and over in his hands.

"Gee!" Ernie ran his finger along the edge. "I bet this old tomahawk has scalped a hundred men. Maybe two hundred!"

The boys forgot all about fishing. They began to dig again furiously.

Thad said, "There's just got to be more stuff around here. Then we'll each have a tomahawk."

However, they did not find another thing, not even an arrowhead.

By now it was getting late. It was time for Ernie to go feed the chickens. He heard Papa calling him. He picked up his spade in one hand. He hesitated. Then he picked up the tomahawk in the other hand. Without looking at Thad, he started down the hill.

"Hey!" Thad called. "Give me back my tomahawk, Ernie."

Ernie stopped and looked back. "It's not your tomahawk. It's mine."

"It's mine," Thad protested. "I found it, didn't I?"

"Maybe you did," Ernie said, "but where did you find it? You found it in my Indian mound, that's where!" He started toward the house carrying the spade and tomahawk in his hands.

"Finders are keepers," Thad called. "Everybody knows that."

"Anything found in my Indian mound belongs to me!" Ernie called. He raced away toward the chicken house clutching the tomahawk tightly in his hand.

Thad started to follow him. Then, instead, he turned around and went home.

That night Ernie would not let the tomahawk out of his sight. He put it by his plate when he sat down to supper.

"Where's Thad?" asked Mama. "We're having burnt-sugar cake for dessert tonight. Thad always likes that."

Ernie looked down at his plate. "Thad went home," he said quickly. He didn't dare look up at Mama. She might guess that something was wrong. She might ask Ernie questions. She might even think that Thad had a right to the tomahawk.

To Ernie's relief Mama did not ask any questions. "Well, I'll save him some cake," she said quietly. "He can get it tomorrow when he comes over to play."

But the next day Thad did not come over.

At first Ernie did not care. He put the tomahawk in his overalls pocket. He took it with him wherever he went. It was his, wasn't it? No matter what Thad said!

That afternoon when chores were over Ernie did not know what to do with himself. He couldn't remember a day for months when Thad hadn't rushed up to the house. Ernie kept listening for Thad's whistle, but all he could hear was the wind.

With Shep for company, he climbed the Indian mound. At the top he looked toward Thad's farm. Maybe Thad would be riding over on his

pony. Maybe he was on his way this very minute. Ernie could see the whole countryside from the top of the mound.

Fields of corn stretched for miles and miles. The corn was high now. Green stalks waved in the dry, hot breeze. Ernie could see everything—everything but Thad. Thad wasn't coming. Maybe he wouldn't ever come.

Ernie stood very still, thinking. Now in the afternoon everything was quiet except the wind. It was a long, sighing wind.

"This time yesterday," Ernie thought, "Thad and I were still friends. We were digging together. Now I'm alone except for Shep and the tomahawk. I still have that, but what fun is a tomahawk if I've taken it away from someone else? That's what I've done," he admitted to himself. "After all, Thad really found it. It's his, not mine."

Suddenly Ernie knew what he had to do. He

had known it all along, really, but now he wanted to do it.

"Come on, Shep. Let's go!"

Ernie started running down the hill, Shep at his heels. He raced across the road. He cut through the fields. He ran and he ran.

When he reached the Hooker place, he saw Thad sitting on the porch steps. That was funny. Thad hardly ever sat still. He was always doing something. But there he was, just sitting. He looked lonesome. Ernie ran up to him and held out the tomahawk. "Here," he said. "It's yours. For keeps."

"Oh!" Thad said. "Thanks."

The two boys looked at each other.

"You know what?" Thad asked.

"No. What?"

"I'll keep it tonight, Ernest. You can have it tomorrow night. We'll take turns," Thad added. "It isn't really mine."

"It isn't only mine either," Ernie said. "It can belong to both of us."

"For keeps," Thad added. "Gee, it sure is a beauty! I bet this old tomahawk has scalped a hundred men."

Ernie grinned. "Maybe two hundred! Come on, let's go back over to my house. Mama's saved you some burnt-sugar cake."

The Wedding

AUNT MARY was getting married. The wedding date was set: September 26, 1908. Thank goodness, she wouldn't move far away. She was going to marry George Bales and live just down the road.

"Will I have to call you Mrs. Bales when you get married?" Ernie asked.

Aunt Mary laughed. "Of course not. I'll always be your Aunt Mary. You're just getting a new uncle, that's all."

"Uncle George," Ernie said, trying the new name. "He's always been Mariam's uncle. Now he'll be mine, too."

Ernie was pleased. He liked his new Uncle George. George Bales did not do things the way other farmers did. He'd rather fuss around all day with his flowers or play the piano. He had a handsome big black square piano.

"That George Bales is a dreamer," Mama said. "I declare, Mary, I think you're marrying him just so you can get that farm of his to working properly again."

Mama was teasing. Aunt Mary knew that. "No," she answered, "I'm marrying him so he'll stop taking me for those rides before breakfast." Now Aunt Mary was teasing.

It was true about the rides. That summer when Ernie and Thad found the tomahawk it had been Mr. Bales who woke Ernie each morning. He woke them all up. Every nice day, early in the morning, they had heard him yell to Aunt Mary to come for a ride.

There George Bales would be, out in front in

his two-wheeled sulky. His mare was so skittish he didn't dare leave her to come up to the door. He would hold on to the reins and yell until Aunt Mary went out and climbed up on the little seat with him. Then away they would go at a fast clip down the road.

Aunt Mary would come back in time for breakfast. She would shake her head. "Who ever heard of going riding before breakfast? What will the neighbors think? I guess I'll have to marry him to stop this foolishness." Then she would laugh, her eyes shining.

Now the wedding was just a week off.

Ernie had never been to a wedding. He was excited. The whole house was in a commotion. It was scrubbed and polished until it shone from top to bottom. The kitchen hummed like a beehive. Ernie had never seen so much beating and mixing and baking going on.

"Let me lick the bowls," he begged.

He liked best of all to lick the batter from the wedding cake. It was white and rich and tasted wonderful.

"It ought to be good," Mama said. "It's got a pound of butter and a dozen eggs in it. Now get out of the kitchen. I don't want you jumping around while the cake is in the oven. You might make it fall."

On the morning of the wedding day Ernie turned the crank of the big ice-cream freezer, out on the back porch. Thad helped. He held the burlap sack tight over the ice and salt packed in the freezer.

Ernie cranked and cranked. Finally he stopped to rub his arm. "It aches," he said.

"My hands are freezing," said Thad.

"All right, you turn the crank for a while."

After that they took turns. Every so often they took off the burlap. Carefully they scraped the ice and salt away from the top of the big inside container. They opened the lid and peered in to see how hard the ice cream was getting. It took a long time for ice cream to freeze, they discovered.

"Gee, I wish I could come to the wedding," Thad said. "I've never seen anybody get married. Besides, it seems like there's going to be some right good eating."

"I wish you could, too," said Ernie. "But Mama says it's going to be a small wedding. Only relations are invited. Will Bales, because he's Uncle George's boy. And Mariam and her folks, because they're the other Bales family. And Uncle Oat and Aunt Frankie Paxton—Aunt Frankie is Papa's sister, you know. We asked Great-aunt Nancy Miller to come from Chicago, but she says she's too old to travel. The preacher is coming, too, of course. Aunt Mary can't get married without him."

Ernie looked up. "But gee, Thad, you're almost a member of our family. I wish we could work it for you to come somehow."

Ernie thought fast as he turned the crank of the freezer. It was getting harder and harder to turn. The ice cream must be almost frozen.

"I know!" he said suddenly. He looked toward the kitchen door. Then he lowered his voice. "Why don't you come over this evening when everybody's busy getting dressed up? I'll be on the lookout. I'll sneak you into the parlor. You can hide under the sofa. Maybe you won't be able to see very much, but you can hear everything that goes on."

Thad grinned. "That's a good idea. But what if they find me? You mama will get mad. And what about the eats? I'll 'most likely starve to death, staying under that sofa all evening."

"Pooh! Nobody will think of looking under the sofa. Everybody will be busy. I can slip you some cake and ice cream." Ernie's eyes were bright. The wedding would be much more fun if Thad were around.

Thad did not need much persuading. One more look at the peach ice cream decided him. Six quarts of it! There would be plenty for everybody. It was all settled.

Papa stepped out on the porch to see how the ice cream was coming along. "What are you two fellows giggling about?" he wanted to know.

"Nothing much," Ernie said and laughed.

The ice cream was firm. Carefully Papa pulled out the wooden paddle from the middle of the container—the "ladder," he called it. Velvety-smooth pink ice cream was clinging to the blades of the paddle. Papa started to scrape it all back into the container.

"Leave some for us," Ernie begged. "Mama said we could lick the ladder."

"All right. Here you are. When you're through, take the ladder in for Mama to wash."

"There's not much to wash," Mama said later. "I see it's been licked clean as a whistle."

"We let Shep finish it off," Ernie said.

"Yes'm," said Thad. "That was mighty good ice cream. I wouldn't mind having some more." He looked at Ernie. They both burst out laughing, but Mama was too busy to pay any attention.

That evening everything went according to plan. At least it did at first. Thad came over early. Ernie was the only one around to see him crawl under the sofa.

Thad stuck his head out. "I didn't get dressed up," he whispered. "I was scared my folks would know I was up to something. I just sneaked out and ran over here."

"That's all right. Nobody's going to see you. Sh! Here comes Mama. Hide quick!"

One last loud whisper came from under the sofa. "Don't forget the ice cream and cake!"

The wedding ceremony was solemn. Mama

played the "Wedding March" on her violin. Ernie stood beside Mariam and watched from the doorway.

Aunt Mary's cheeks were pink. She looked pretty in her new chocolate-brown suit. Uncle George stood very straight in his best Sunday clothes. The preacher began to read from his black book. The reading didn't last long. Ernie was surprised to learn how quickly people could get married.

When it was over, everybody began to laugh and crowd around the bride and bridegroom. Ernie started over, too. Then he stopped. He saw Aunt Mary was crying. "Because I'm so happy," she sobbed.

"Grownups sure act funny," Ernie thought. But in a way he knew how Aunt Mary felt—sort of sad and glad all at once.

Then the kissing began. Aunt Mary kissed Uncle George. She kissed Mama. She kissed almost everybody in the room, and everybody kissed her back.

"Not me," Ernie said to himself. "Nobody's going to kiss me."

In a panic he looked around for someplace to hide. Quickly he darted behind the sofa and ducked out of sight. "Move over," he whispered in Thad's ear.

Together the boys crouched on the floor under the sofa. They listened to the babble of sound in the crowded room. Everybody was talking at once. The boys got the giggles.

Suddenly they heard Aunt Mary. "Where's Ernest?" she cried. "Isn't he going to congratulate us? Where is that boy?"

"Why, he was right here a minute ago." That was Papa's voice.

"Where did he go?" Aunt Mary asked again. The boys heard people calling, "Ernest! Ernest, where are you?"

Ernie was laughing so hard he had to put his hands over his mouth.

Thad said, "You'd better get out of here—quick. They'll hear you."

"Not me. I'm staying right here till the fuss is over. I'll be safe here."

All at once a hand pulled up the sofa cover. A streak of light shone full on the boys' faces. There was Mariam on her hands and knees. She was staring at them.

"Here he is!" she called. "I found him. And not only him!"

Shamefaced, the two boys crawled out. Ernie gave Aunt Mary a shy grin. He braced himself for a scolding. She did not scold him, but he was glad he had braced himself. She kissed him. She kissed him right there in front of everybody!

Thad started for the door. Aunt Mary caught hold of his arm. "Don't run off, Thad. If you wanted that much to see us get married, I reckon you can stay. You're practically a member of the family, anyway!" She gave Thad a kiss, too.

"Besides," said Mama, "it's time to cut the wedding cake. It's a right good cake, if I do say so myself. Better stay and have a piece."

"Thank you," Thad said.

"And some peach ice cream," Ernie added.

"Thank you," said Thad again.

The two boys grinned at each other. Weddings were all right. That is, they were all right after the kissing was over and done with.

The Visitor

THE HOUSE seemed strange without Aunt Mary bustling around, helping Mama. Now she bustled around the Bales house, helping Uncle George. Ernie saw her almost every day.

"Remember you've got two homes now, Ernest," Aunt Mary said. "I miss you when you don't stop in after school for a spell."

"That's right, Shag," put in Uncle George. He gave a playful tug at Ernie's curly hair. "Just make yourself at home. Want to hear a new piece on the piano?"

That year Ernie did not have much time for listening to the piano. After school he had more and more work to do on Papa's farm, especially when spring came. Papa was very busy with the plowing then.

"Next year I'm going to put you to the plow," Papa said. "I began plowing when I was nine years old. There's no reason why you can't. This spring you must feed the animals. And there's always wood you can chop in your spare time."

One day in April Ernie was chopping wood after school. He wanted to go down to Aunt Mary's or over to Thad's. But he couldn't go anywhere until he finished a pile of wood.

Ernie stopped to give Shep a pat. "Chopping wood just isn't your favorite thing, is it, Shep? Mine either."

Shep wagged his feathery tail. Then he pricked up his ears and began to bark. Ernie looked up. He saw a stranger coming around to the back door. Shep growled. He didn't like tramps. Mama didn't either.

"Ragged, shiftless creatures," she called them. "Always asking for a handout," she would add. "They'll eat you out of house and home, and never do a lick of work in return."

Now Shep barked fiercely. Ernie grabbed Shep's collar and held on tight.

"Will he bite?" the tramp asked Ernie. He didn't sound scared, just curious. "A dog is supposed to be man's best friend, you know."

"Yes, he's mine. I won't let him bite," Ernie said. "There, Shep, it's all right. Quiet, boy!"

Shep growled a little, but he stood still.

Ernie looked at the tramp. His clothes were in rags. He had a nice face, though. It was brown from the sun. Now he smiled at Ernie.

"That's a good watchdog you've got there. I don't aim to do any harm. Just thought maybe your folks would give me something in the way of refreshments. It's been quite a spell since I ate breakfast."

"My folks aren't here," said Ernie. "Papa's out plowing, and Mama's gone to a Ladies' Aid meeting. I'm chopping wood."

"I see you are. You're pretty small to swing that big ax. Now me—I'm pretty handy with an ax."

Ernie looked surprised. "I thought tramps didn't like to work."

"I didn't say anything about liking it, did I? A lick of work now and then never hurt a body, though. Besides, I'm not exactly a tramp. I'm just a wanderer."

The man took off his battered hat and made a funny, sweeping bow. "Willie the Wanderer—that's what they call me. At your service. Here, I'll finish off this wood for you."

Willie took the ax and began to swing. In no time he had the wood all cut to lengths. Ernie was kept busy stacking it up in a neat pile.

"Now, then," Willie said with a grin, "my stomach tells me that the spell of time since break-fast isn't growing any shorter. Got any ideas?"

Ernie laughed. He liked Willie. Even Shep was making up to him now. Surely Mama wouldn't mind if Ernie took Willie into the kitchen and gave him something to eat.

While Willie washed his hands at the pump, Ernie got things out of the cupboard. There was ham, and a loaf of homemade bread, and some apple pie. Ernie ran out to the springhouse and came back with a pitcher of milk.

"What a feast, my lad!" said Willie, as he ate a thick sandwich. "A feast fit for the gods—and, I might add, for Willie the Wanderer himself."

Ernie liked the funny way the man talked. Between bites, Willie told Ernie all about his wanderings and the sights he had seen.

"I follow the sun," he said, "and I follow the spring. This year I followed the flowers from the Gulf of Mexico on up to Indiana. You've got some mighty pretty wild flowers blooming here in April. There isn't anything in the world so pretty as a patch of pink arbutus flowers. You find them under the dead brown leaves in the woods. And the scent of them! Did you ever get down on your knees and take a whiff of arbutus? Smells better than anything on earth."

Willie paused a moment, then added, "Unless maybe it's this apple pie of your mama's. Besides, you can't eat arbutus, and I find it easy to consume this delectable pie."

Willie helped himself to another piece. Sugary juice ran out of the pie all over his plate. Willie scooped it up with his spoon.

Willie went on and on, telling about the fine places he had been, the fine people he had talked to. "Yes, sir, people are the same the world over. Give a fellow a chance, and you'll find he's just folks, the same as you and me."

"Gee, I'd like to be a wanderer!" said Ernie.

"No regular chores to do every day. I'd see cities and farms all over the country, and talk to people, all kinds of people. Or, more like it, listen to them talk. And I'd always be moving." He sighed.

A shadow fell over the table. Ernie looked up, startled. Mama was standing in the doorway.

"Ernest Taylor Pyle! What is this tramp doing in my kitchen?" She sounded cross.

Ernie jumped up from his chair. "He's not really a tramp, Mama," he explained. "He's a—well, he's a wanderer."

"Same thing, as far as I can see," Mama said. She turned to Willie. "Now I'll thank you to move along, Mister."

"Yes, ma'am." Willie got to his feet.

Mama went on: "No work, no food. That's the rule around here."

Ernie spoke up. "Oh, but Willie chopped wood! He did work."

Mama looked as if she were going to smile. But all she said was, "He did your work for you, you mean. That's not quite the same thing."

Ernie started to protest, but Willie picked up his hat. "Never mind, son," he said. "Time I was leaving, anyhow. Willie the Wanderer never stays long enough to wear out his welcome."

He gave Ernie and Mama his funny, sweeping bow. "Much obliged for your hospitality." Then he went out the door.

Ernie started after him.

"Ernest," Mama called, "you stay right here. Don't you go bothering with the likes of him—bowing and scraping all over the place, like a duke or something!"

Ernie looked at her in dismay. "He was nice, Mama, real nice. He was just folks, like you and me and Papa."

"Mighty queer folks, I'd call him. A tramp's a tramp, no matter what fancy name he calls himself. Willie the Wanderer! I never heard the like."

"But, Mama!" Ernie looked at her helplessly. How could he make her understand how he felt? And poor Willie! Mama must have hurt his feelings, shooing him off like that—as if he were a chicken.

Suddenly Ernie felt he could not bear it. He had to find Willie. He ran out the door and around to the front of the house. Willie was nowhere in sight.

Ernie ran over to the Indian mound. He scrambled to the top, with Shep bounding along beside him. Maybe he could see Willie from the top of the mound. He could hear Mama calling him, but he paid no attention.

Ernie looked eagerly up and down the road. In the west the setting sun blinded him, so that he could not see. Toward the east a cloud of dust billowed out behind a horse and buggy. The dust hid the road from sight.

"Oh, Shep," Ernie said, "I can't see which way he went! If I knew I'd follow him right now. You and me. We'd catch up with him. We'd stick to him, too. Maybe he'd let us be wanderers. But I don't know which way to start. We'd miss him for sure."

Ernie strained his eyes, looking to the east and then to the west. But nowhere could he see the tall figure of a man swinging down the road. Willie was gone.

"Maybe he's gone into the woods," Ernie said aloud. "Maybe he's hunting for some of that pink flower he was talking about. Anyhow—" and here his voice choked—"Willie's gone!"

He threw himself down on the ground. Shep came over and licked his face.

"Ernest!" It was Papa calling somewhere near the house.

Ernie raised his head but did not answer.

"Ernest!" Papa was coming nearer. "It's 'way past time to feed the chickens."

Ernie scrambled to his feet. He kicked at a near-by tree stump. "Chickens, always chickens!" he said disgustedly.

"Ernest Pyle!" Papa was coming up the hill after him now.

Ernie sighed. Then he started slowly down the hill toward the chicken house. Shep trotted along at his side.

"The way we look after those chickens," Ernie said to Shep, "you'd think they were just as important as folks!"

Then he went on down the hill.

Ernie Goes Visiting

GREAT-AUNT Nancy Miller in Chicago kept urging Mama to visit her.

"I'm not so young as I used to be," she wrote. "It's hard for me to travel. I want to hear about Mary's wedding. Why don't you come to Chicago to see me? Bring Ernest, too. Right next door there's a nice family with four children. Ernest can play with them and won't be lonely."

Mama was so busy she kept putting off the trip. Ernie was busy, too. All summer he helped Papa in the fields, and in the winter there was school. It was spring again before Mama made definite plans to go to Chicago. She decided to go during Ernie's Easter vacation so that he wouldn't miss any school.

Ernie was excited. He wanted to ride on the train. He wanted to see a big city. He wanted to see Aunt Nancy, too. For years she had sent him post cards for his collection.

"There's just one thing wrong with the visit," Ernie thought. He was hurrying home from Thad's house the day before he and his mother were to leave. "Those kids who live next door to Aunt Nancy. City kids! They'll probably be stuck-up. They'll think I'm just a country jake. They won't want to have anything to do with me, most likely. I hope Aunt Nancy doesn't make us play together."

In the house Ernie found Mama baking things for Aunt Nancy. An angel-food cake was cooling. Mama was taking a batch of cookies out of the oven.

"Aunt Nancy wants my recipe for these molasses cookies," she said. "You copy it out of the book for her."

Ernie sat down at the kitchen table with pencil and paper. He was in the fourth grade now and knew how to write well. Next to geography, reading and writing were his favorite subjects.

Carefully Ernie copied the recipe out of Mama's cookbook. First he wrote down the list of things to go into the cookies. "Ingredients" they were called.

"Copy the directions, too," Mama said.

Ernie wrote the first line: "Bring molasses to a boil."

Then he had an idea. He chewed on the end of his pencil for a while. Then he bent over his paper. He wrote and erased and rewrote.

"What are you doing, Ernest?" his mother asked after a while. "You're taking a long time."

Ernie brushed his hair out of his eyes. "I've made a poem out of it. See?"

Mama looked at the paper. Ernie had made up a rhyme to go with each line in the directions. Altogether the rhymes made a little poem. Mama read the poem aloud.

"Bring molasses to a boil.
This is fun; no work, no toil.
Add shortening, ginger, soda in milk.
This will make it smooth as silk.
Add flour next. And then the salt.
When this is done, you call a halt.
Set aside till really chill.
Put it on the window sill.
Toss mixture on a floured board.
Roll quite thin to feed a horde.
Dip cutter in flour, then cut in shape.
You won't need a measuring tape.
Place near together on buttered sheet.
They'll all look nice and very neat.
Put in oven eight minutes—or ten.
Take cookies out, let cool, and then
We kids will suddenly appear.
Just watch those cookies disappear!"

Mama laughed. "There's more truth than poetry in those last two lines," she said. "But it's a nice poem, Ernest, and I know Aunt Nancy will like it."

"Oh," Ernie protested, "I'm not going to give this to her! She'll think I'm showing off if I take her all these silly rhymes. Here, I'll make her a plain copy, just the way it's written in the book."

Mama tried to persuade him to save the rhymes for Aunt Nancy, but he wouldn't. "Well, then," she said, "I'll keep them myself. Maybe you'll be a real poet when you grow up."

"Not me. I'm not going to stay home and write stuff like Longfellow and James Whitcomb Riley. I'm going to do something exciting." Ernie's eyes sparkled.

"Maybe I'll be a race driver at the new Speedway in Indianapolis—like Ralph de Palma or Barney Oldfield. I'll race the fastest car ever made and I'll win the biggest race. Then I'll take my car and go all over the country—all over the world. I'll be a sort of wanderer."

"Well, we'll see," said Mama drily. "Meantime you're just going up to Chicago, and you'll ride on the C. & E. I. local. The train hasn't broken any speed records yet that I have ever heard of. But it hasn't broken any necks, either, like some of those fast racing cars."

THE TRAIN RIDE

Chicago, Chicago. We're going to Chicago! "That's what the train wheels are saying," Ernie decided. "It's like a song. Sometimes it's loud and sometimes soft, but that's what they sing over and over."

Ernie turned away from the window to ask Mama if she heard the song, too, but Mama's eyes were closed. Her head rested against the soft plush of the seat. The curly feather on her new spring hat nodded up and down with the motion of the train.

Ernie watched it for a minute. "Even Mama's feather keeps time to the song," he thought. *Chicago, Chicago. We're going to Chicago!*

He looked up at the ceiling. The hanging lamp was swinging back and forth over the aisle of the day coach. It was keeping time, too. *Chicago, Chicago!*

Cheerful, creaking sounds came from the varnished woodwork in the car. *We're going to Chicago!* it murmured.

Ernie looked at the passengers. How could they read or sleep when the train ride was so exciting! He glanced out the window again. He had been gazing out for hours, but he did not want to miss a single thing. He blew the soot off the window sill and leaned on his elbow. It was strange how heavy his eyelids felt.

Ernie tried not to watch the telephone wires. They seemed to stretch and sag, stretch and sag, as the train clicked past the poles. They made him a little dizzy. Ernie closed his eyes. The sound of the whistle drifted back from the engine: *Chi-ca-go, Chi—caaa—goooo!*

Ernie couldn't remember the rest of the trip. He must have fallen asleep. Suddenly he heard the conductor call, "Dearborn Station, Chicago. All out. Don't forget your valises!"

Mama shook him and told him to put on his cap and coat and rubbers. She gathered up her baskets and parcels, and Ernie took the valise. Then they climbed down the steps of the car and walked into the brick station.

Everything was confusing. There were a million lights everywhere. There were a thousand doors. And there were a million people, all rushing in different directions. Ernie wished Aunt Nancy had come to meet them. Even though Mama had visited Chicago before, how would she ever find Aunt Nancy's house?

Mama was just as calm as she had been in the

depot at Dana. She read over the directions Aunt Nancy had sent. Then she led Ernie straight out of the station, and down the street to a corner. Ernie stumbled along with the heavy valise. He had never seen so many buildings or so many cars. He had never seen so many hansom cabs or wagons or streetcars, either.

Somehow he and Mama got on a streetcar for the South Side. It was crowded with people going home from work. A man gave Mama his seat, but Ernie had to stand. The streetcar started and stopped a million times. Each time Ernie nearly lost his balance. Just when he decided that he would have to ride this way forever, the conductor shouted, "Sixty-third street!"

Mama looked up. "This is where we get off."

She had to ask a lady on the corner how to find the way to Aunt Nancy's street. They started walking again. It seemed to Ernie that there were miles of sidewalk and houses. The valise grew heavier every minute. Then they turned into a quiet side street. "There's the house," said Mama, "and Aunt Nancy is at the window watching for us!"

When they reached the door Aunt Nancy came out to meet them. She gave him a hug and said, "Why, Ernest, you look dead tired."

Ernie shook his head. "He's hungry, most likely," said Mama.

Aunt Nancy brought Ernie a glass of milk. Mama unpacked her molasses cookies and gave him a few. During supper Aunt Nancy and Mama talked busily. Ernie thought about Shep and Thad and the farm and Papa, and before long he began to feel sleepy.

He hardly remembered going upstairs and going to bed. Aunt Nancy came in to tell him good night. She said something about the children next door, but Ernie was too sleepy to answer. Wheels were still going around inside his head.

But now they were singing *Chicago, Chicago, at last you're in Chicago!*

CITY KIDS

Next morning when Ernie woke up there was a worry nagging at the back of his mind. What was it? He was in Chicago, wasn't he?

He jumped out of bed, ran to the window and looked out. Right next door, so close he could almost touch it, was a brown frame house. Of course, that was it! Those city kids! He might have to play with them.

Ernie worried as he dressed. "I won't know what to talk to them about," he thought. "I won't know any of their old games, most likely. I hope they won't come!"

They did come, however. Right after breakfast the doorbell rang. In filed the four children from next door. Aunt Nancy introduced them.

"Ernest, this is Alberta and little Margie Johnson, and these are their brothers, Tom and Stephen. Their mother has sent them over to play with you. Children, this is Ernest."

"Hullo," they murmured.

"Hullo," Ernie said in a low voice.

"Now get your cap, Ernest, and all of you go outside to play."

Ernie took a quick look at the caps the boys were holding. They were a plain dark blue. He didn't want the boys to see his. It was different. It had big black and white checks. They would make fun of it for sure. Hastily he grabbed it off the hat rack and stuffed it in his pocket.

Mama came out in the hall. "You'd better put on your rubbers, Ernest."

Ernie took a quick look at the Johnson children's feet. They weren't wearing rubbers. "Oh, no," he protested. "It's nice outside." He'd better get out before Mama insisted. He opened the door and ran across the front porch and down the steps. The Johnson children followed. They all stopped on the front walk. They looked at one another uncertainly.

Why didn't somebody say something? Tom was the biggest; he ought to start things. But when Ernie looked at Tom, Tom just put his hands in his pockets and glanced away.

"He's probably mad because his mama made him come over," Ernie thought. "Maybe they're all mad. They don't want to play with me."

Ernie looked at Stephen and the girls. They stared back. This silence was awful. Finally Ernie cleared his throat. "What do you all want to do?' he asked desperately.

Tom swallowed. "Why, I don't care," he said.

Alberta spoke. "What do you want to do?" She smiled anxiously at Ernie.

Suddenly Ernie understood. "Why," he thought in amazement, "they aren't mad at all.

They're just bashful like me! They've probably been worrying about me, thinking maybe I wouldn't want to play with them!"

Ernie was so surprised at his discovery that he laughed out loud. He had an inspiration. "What would you do if I weren't here?" he asked.

Tom and Steve both answered at once. "Play with our automobiles."

"Automobiles! What kind? Where are they? Can I see them?"

Now the Johnsons all talked at once.

"Sure."

"Let's go."

"They're over at our house."

"We made them ourselves. They don't have real engines, but they go fast."

The children ran around to the back of the Johnson's house. From under the back porch, the boys pulled out two homemade cars.

"Gee, they're dandies!" Ernie said admiringly.

Tom and Steve beamed. Proudly they showed off the engine boxes, with the cans nailed on top to look like radiator caps. There were larger cans nailed on the sides to look like headlights.

"See, here is where you sit," Tom said. "Go on, Ernie, try it."

Delighted, Ernie sat down in the driver's seat of one car.

"Here's where you put your feet, on this bar here," Tom said.

"Here's the rope you steer with," Steve added. "See how it's fastened to the front axle?"

"Does it really work?" Ernie asked.

"Of course it works. Somebody can run ahead and pull, or somebody can push from behind. Or the car can go by itself down a hill."

Ernie's eyes sparkled. "Is there a hill around here?" he asked.

"Yes, over in Jackson Park. It's just a few blocks away. Want to go there?"

"Let's go!"

Ernie was delighted with Jackson Park. "It's almost like country in the city," he said. He was helping to pull the cars up a slope. "But this hill isn't as high as our Indian mound at home."

Suddenly Ernie had an idea. "I know what," he said. "We could play that this is the Speedway. You know, the new Speedway we've got over in Indiana. We could even have automobile races if you wanted to."

"Yes, let's do," Tom said. "How are the races run? Have you ever been to the Speedway?"

"Not yet," Ernie said, "but Papa's going to take me someday. I know all about the race, though. I look at all the pictures and read about it in the papers. My favorite driver is Ralph De Palma. I'll be him when it's my turn to race. He drives a Fiat sometimes."

Now Tom spoke up. "You're company, Ernie, so you can drive in the first race. When it's my turn to drive, I'm going to be Barney Oldfield. I know about him."

"Who can I be?" Steve asked. "Who is somebody else famous?"

Ernie thought for a moment. Then he said, "You can be Wild Bob Burman. He's good, too. And your car can be a Blitzen Benz."

By this time they were swinging the small cars around at the top of the hill.

Alberta asked, "Who can I be? I want to be someone." She looked at Ernie.

Ernie thought a minute. "You can be a riding mechanic for Wild Bob Burman, and Tom can be mine. You two give us a push and then hop on the back. We'll need you if we have a blowout."

"Don't forget me." Little Margie was jumping up and down. "Let me do something. What can I do?"

"You're too little," Tom said. "You just keep out of the way."

"Yes, you're too little," Alberta said. "You just stand here and watch."

Margie's eyes filled with tears. "I'm not too little!" she cried.

Ernie looked down at her. He could imagine how she felt. He hesitated. Then he said, "I know what." He pulled his cap out of his pocket. "The men at the real Speedway have a black-and-white checked flag at the finish line. They wave it when the winner crosses the line. You can do that, Margie. Like this."

Ernie raised his cap high above his head. Then, holding his arm stiff, he quickly brought the cap down to the ground beside one of the cars. "See? That way. You drop it beside the car that crosses the finish line first. You tell which one wins. That's important."

Margie laughed and nodded. " 'Portant," she repeated happily.

"Now take the cap down to the bottom of the

j
921
Pyle

697977

Wilson, Ellen
Ernie Pyle, boy from back home.

MAR2370
MAR2370 David Humphrey
APR2870 J 1935
APR2870 J 1935
MAY6 70 Robin Nelson
MAY1370 Shelly Hall
JUL1770 A12256
JUL1770 A12256
AUG3170 A13410
NOV1870 A11967

305

mrs Wendling
2-19-86

A10648 NOV2570

hill," Ernie said. "Down there by that bunch of trees. That can be the finish line."

As Margie ran off, Alberta looked admiringly at Ernie. "It was lucky you had that kind of cap—just the right colors."

"Yes," Tom said. "I wish I had one like that instead of this old plain green one."

"Why don't you turn your cap around so the visor is in back?" Ernie suggested. "That's the way the real drivers wear them."

"All right," Tom said. Steve turned his cap around, too.

"That's the way," sail Ernie. "Come on, time for the race."

He and Steve settled themselves in the drivers' seats. Tom and Alberta stood behind, and took hold of the rear box seats.

"Everybody ready?" Steve asked. "One, two, three—shove!"

Tom and Alberta each gave a push. The cars

began to move. Holding on the cars, the riding mechanics kept pushing and running. Then, as the cars gathered speed, they hopped aboard.

The "Fiat" and the "Benz" ran smoothly at first, side by side. Alberta began to yell, "Come on, Wild Bob Burman!"

Tom jumped off Ernie's car and gave one more push. The car rolled faster, but when Tom hopped on again the car swerved. Ernie sawed at the ropes. The car was hard to steer. Ernie kept pulling too hard, first on one side, then on the other.

"Come on, De Palma!" shouted Tom. "Wild Bob Burman is ahead!"

Ernie glanced up long enough to see Steve going faster and faster down the slope. He was far ahead. Suddenly Ernie's wheels ran over a large bump. His car lurched to one side and zigzagged wildly. Tom laughed and yelled and hung on tight. Ernie laughed, too, and sawed at the

steering ropes. It took him a minute to get back on the track.

By this time Steve was at the bottom of the hill. He made a wide turn and brought his car to a standstill right beside the trees on the finish line.

Margie raised the black-and-white-checked cap high and brought it down as Ernie had shown her. "Steve wins," she screamed. "He wins the race!"

The "Fiat" rushed down toward the finish line. Ernie's car was going so fast he could not stop. He turned just in time to keep from running head-on into the trees. Finally he came to a stop right in the middle of a clump of bushes.

Ernie and his mechanic sat there a minute, laughing. The others crowded around and helped pull the car out of the bushes.

Ernie clapped Steve on the back. "Wild Bob Burman's the winner! Congratulations, Bob."

"Thanks, De Palma. You'll win after you catch onto the steering," Steve said. "You can't pull too hard on the ropes. Come on, let's try it again, Ernie."

The races went on and on. Ernie had never had so much fun. Finally, when the noon whistles blew, they all went home for dinner. By Aunt Nancy's walk the Johnsons said, "Can you come out and play this afternoon, Ernie?"

"Sure. Sometime I want to see the rest of Jackson Park, too."

"Oh, we'll show you the park, all right," Steve said. "The Lagoons and the Wooded Island."

"And the lake," Tom added.

"And the Field Museum," said Alberta. "We'll show you everything because you showed us how to play Speedway."

Little Margie laughed. "Speedway," she repeated. "That's 'portant." She handed Ernie his checked cap.

This time Ernie did not stuff it into his pocket. He put it on his head. He put it on backward, just as he had said the great race drivers did.

As he ran up Aunt Nancy's steps, Tom called after him, "Tomorrow maybe Mama will take us all to Marshall Field's store. I want to buy a cap just like yours!"

A Proud Moment

ERNIE's first visit to Chicago was too short to suit him. He wanted to go back, but as soon as he got home he was busy again with school and chores on the farm.

When he and his classmates entered the fifth grade that fall, their teacher started them writing compositions for their English class.

One afternoon Ernie and Mariam were on their way home from school.

"What are you going to write about for tomorrow, Ernest?" Mariam asked. "You know Miss Campbell said our composition should be about somebody's 'proud moment.' "

"Golly, I don't know!" Ernie said. "I can't think of many proud moments. Can you?"

Mariam swung her long braids back over her shoulders. "I'll write about a king or a queen. Or maybe a great singer or somebody. People like that have lots of proud moments."

Ernie laughed. "Well, I don't know many kings or queens, or great singers either, for that matter. I'll have to pick someone else, I reckon. Meantime, I have to help Papa build a corncrib this afternoon. I'll see you tomorrow." Ernie gave a playful tug at one of Mariam's braids as he started off.

While he helped build the corncrib, Ernie tried to choose a subject for his composition. He thought about it all through supper, too. Maybe he should write about Napoleon or George Washington or some other great man.

"I reckon I don't know much about how famous people really felt, though," he thought.

"In the history books they all sound pretty stiff and solemn."

Mama broke in on his thoughts. "Ernest, when are you going fishing again? We haven't had a good mess of catfish for a long time." She began to laugh. "Remember the first catfish you ever caught?"

Papa chuckled. "That sure was a surprise, the way you caught that fish. I'll never forget how you looked when you brought it up to the house."

Ernie grinned. He had forgotten all about his first fish. Why, he had caught it over five years ago! He was only five years old then.

For weeks afterward Papa and Mama had teased him about the funny way he had caught his fish.

"Since then," Ernie said, "I bet I've gone fishing a hundred times or more down in Mr. Webster's crick. I bet I've caught hundreds of sunnies and catfish, but not one of them was so exciting as that first one. I sure was proud of my first fish, wasn't I?"

Ernie stopped eating, his fork halfway to his mouth. "Of course!" he thought. "That was a proud moment. Now I have something to write about, and it won't be too solemn, either."

JUST ORDINARY PEOPLE

The next day in English class, Miss Campbell said, "I am not going to collect your papers the way I usually do. Today I want you to read your compositions aloud to the whole class."

Ernie looked at her in dismay. That was the last thing in the world he wanted to do. He hoped Miss Campbell wouldn't get around to calling on him.

Miss Campbell called on Mariam first. Mariam stood up straight by her desk. She read her composition in a clear voice. It was about how proud young Victoria had felt when she was crowned Queen of England.

Ernie thought it was a wonderful composition. His own would sound pretty silly after that.

Another girl was called on. She read about Mrs. Abraham Lincoln and how proud she had been the day she moved into the White House as First Lady of the United States.

Ernie grew more nervous. Had everybody else written about famous people?

Thad was next. His piece was short. It was on General Washington—how he must have felt when he took command of the Army.

By this time Ernie was feeling miserable. Why hadn't he had the sense to write about somebody important! He could hardly listen to the others read.

"Ernest," came Miss Campbell's voice, "we have just time enough for your composition. We'll hear it now."

Ernie twisted in his seat. "I reckon I must have left mine at home," he muttered.

"What's that paper on your desk? Isn't that your composition?" Miss Campbell sounded impatient.

"Well, it was, but—" Ernie rushed on—"I've got a better idea now. I want to write about—well, about Napoleon. I'll do mine over and read it tomorrow."

"Nonsense! You will read it right now. What is the title?"

Ernie swallowed hard. "It's called 'A Boy's Proud Moment.' "

Slowly he got to his feet. He began to read in a low voice:

"It was a hot day. A five-year-old boy went fishing. He went fishing down in Mr. Webster's crick."

Miss Campbell interrupted. " 'Creek'—not

'crick,' Ernest. In the dictionary you will find it is spelled c-r-e-e-k. And do speak up. Don't mumble."

"Yes, ma'am," Ernie said. He went on in a louder voice:

"He took a worm out of the old tomato can. He put it on the hook."

Out of the corner of his eye Ernie saw Mariam shudder.

"Then he dropped it in the crick—I mean creek—and fished. He didn't get a bite. The sun grew hotter and hotter.

"Finally the boy decided to go mud-crawling. The creek wasn't deep enough for real swimming. Anyhow, the boy didn't know how to swim."

A smothered giggle came from Thad, who put one hand over his mouth.

Ernie went on:

"So he took off his overalls and stepped into the stream. The water was only a foot deep. It felt good on his bare feet and on his legs. Then the boy laid down on his stomach."

Miss Campbell interrupted again. "'Lay' down, not 'laid.'"

"Yes, ma'am. 'Lay.'

"—lay down on his stomach. The water was nice and cool. It felt good."

Ernie stopped reading and glanced around the room uncomfortably.

Miss Campbell looked at Ernest. "Is that all?" she asked.

"Well, just about all."

"Read it to the end, Ernest."

Ernie hurried on:

"All of a sudden he felt something tickle his stomach. It was inside his underwear."

At this giggles came from different parts of the room. Ernie's face grew red. But he kept on:

"Then he found he had caught a fish, after all. It wriggled in his—er—underwear. The boy grabbed it. It was the first fish he had ever caught. It was a catfish, eight inches long. He took it home and had it for supper. That was a proud moment for the young fisherman."

Abruptly Ernie sat down. Everybody was laughing. "At least the kids enjoyed it," he thought. Ernie did not dare look at Miss Campbell. She would scold him for sure.

"Well, Ernest," she said, "your composition is certainly different. I am inclined to think it is one of the best, too. Sometimes it is good to write about things and people we know. You seem to know this boy pretty well."

The teacher smiled at Ernie.

She went on: "I do think you ought to keep a dictionary handy. Then you won't write such things as 'crick' and 'laid down.' Now it is time for arithmetic."

Ernie sighed with relief. English class was over. But it hadn't turned out too badly after all, he thought.

"Seems like it's all right, after all, to write about an ordinary person," Ernie said to himself, "instead of always writing about generals and such."

The 500-Mile Race

"I BET everybody in the whole United States is here at the Speedway today!" Ernie said.

Papa laughed. "Not quite. Mama and Aunt Mary and Uncle George stayed home, remember? But it certainly looks as if nobody else stayed home."

It was May 30, 1912. Papa and Ernie and Thad were settling into their seats in one of the grandstands at the Indianapolis Speedway.

Thad sighed happily. "I'd rather be here than anywhere else in the whole world."

"So would I," Ernie said. "I'd rather see the 500-mile race than anything in the world. I didn't mind missing the shorter races they had the first couple of years. But now they have the 500—why, that's the biggest auto race in the whole country!"

Ernie's eyes were big as he looked around. Flags were snapping in the breeze. The air was gay with music from the band.

It was still early. Thousands of people were pouring through the gates. The paddock—an enclosed field near the track—and the infield were filling up with hundreds and hundreds and hundreds of cars.

The two boys from the country were overwhelmed by the crowds and by the bigness of everything. The brick track looped in a huge oval for two and a half miles. The bricks gleamed in the hot morning sun.

"It looks like a big red saucer," said Ernie. He looked at one of the steeply banked curves. "The drivers have smashups on those curves," he went on. "Sometimes they get hurt there, too." He shuddered.

"Don't forget this, boys." Papa sounded serious. "The 500-mile race isn't just a race for thrills. It's not just a race for big prize money, either. It's a race to test cars.

"The drivers and mechanics test engines and tires and gasoline—everything that makes a car run. When the drivers zoom around that track two hundred times, they learn a lot. What they learn about cars there makes it safer for us ordinary folks to drive autos."

Papa smiled at Ernie. "The Pyles are going to have a car one of these days. Even if it's a Model-T Ford instead of one of those fancy cars." He pointed. "There they are, down by the repair pits."

Eagerly Ernie and Thad stared at the low, powerful cars lining up by the pits. For months the boys had read about those special cars in the

Dana *News*. But the pictures they had seen were nothing compared with the cars themselves. These looked dazzling in the bright May sun.

Ernie caught his breath. "They look like wild-cats crouching," he said.

Excitedly the boys picked out their favorites.

"There's Ralph De Palma's car!" Ernie cried. "That Mercedes. See? It's Number Four. De Palma's just sliding out of it and going over to his pit. See, Thad?"

Ernie gazed in awe at his hero. "He's going to win today."

"Pooh!" said Thad. "He can't beat Joe Dawson. There's Joe in that blue National, Number Eight. I'm for him 'cause he's an Indianapolis guy. Look at that classy National, would you!"

Papa grinned. "You're both wrong. I think the Stutz will win. That's the driver there—Gil Anderson. He was best in the trials. That's why he's Number One. Look at that flashy red car, too, the Fiat. That's my second choice. People say Teddy Tetzlaff is a terror at the wheel."

"They call him 'Terrible Teddy,'" said Ernie. "But De Palma is a better driver. He's a good sport too, win or lose. That's why I'm for him."

Ernie turned to Papa. "What time is it? Isn't it almost ten o'clock?"

"Now don't get so excited, Ernest. We've got almost an hour yet before the starting bomb. The race itself will last about six hours, don't forget. There's a long day ahead of us."

As they waited, the boys looked over all twenty-four cars. There were Stutzes, Fiats, Nationals, Marquette-Buicks, Mercers, and a dozen others. They were getting a final checkup.

"Gee, I'd like to be down in those repair pits!" Thad said. "Those mechanics are almost as important as the drivers."

Papa agreed. "A race can be won or lost in the pits. During a race a driver has to stop by his pit if he's in trouble. Repair teams work fast. Every second counts. A minute's delay might lose the race for the driver."

Papa pointed. "See the photographers coming out of their stand? They're going to take pictures. Those cars won't look so shiny at the end of the race!"

Ernie looked at the little white stand. "Who are those other guys sitting there?"

"Those are the newspapermen. They write up the race. They say next year there's going to be a brand-new stand, big enough for the reporters and judges and timers. I read that it's going to look like a big Chinese pagoda."

Papa smiled down at Ernie. "How would you like to be a newspaperman someday? Then you'd get to sit in the pagoda. You'd have the best seat in the place."

"Oh, I don't know. I always thought the best seat in the place was a driver's seat."

Papa snorted. "It's the hottest, too, don't forget—and the most dangerous."

"What time is it?" asked Ernie impatiently. "When is the race going to begin?"

Papa glanced at his watch. "It should start any time now. Yes, look, boys. The drivers are climbing in."

Ernie watched every move De Palma made. The great driver settled in behind his steering wheel. He adjusted his goggles. His riding mechanic slipped in beside him.

Thad watched Joe Dawson. Papa looked first at Gil Anderson, then at Terrible Teddy in his bright red uniform. "I like the looks of Wild Bob Burman, too," he said.

Slowly the drivers brought their cars around in formation. They lined up in five rows. There were five cars in each row except the last. It had only four.

In the lead was the pacemaker car. Mr. Carl

Fisher, president of the Speedway company, would set the pace in his Stutz.

At exactly two minutes after ten the starting bomb went off with a terrific bang. Mr. Fisher led off. The others followed. They had agreed to go at only forty miles an hour this first time around the track. They kept the places of their line-up. The cars swung around the oval, back to the starting tape. After this first lap the pace-maker car drew over to the inside of the track and stopped.

At another signal bomb the green starting flag was dropped. The cars shot over the tape.

The crowd roared. The race was on!

"Come on, De Palma!" Ernie yelled.

THE THIRD LAP FROM THE END

Before the racers were halfway around the track, they were all spread out. Terrible Teddy

was leading. His car was a streak of red out in front of the others.

It was not until the third lap that De Palma caught up. In a tremendous burst of speed his Mercedes shot past the red Fiat. Ernie cheered.

At the end of fifty miles Joe Dawson and Teddy Tetzlaff were both snapping at De Palma's heels. But De Palma kept the lead. The roar of the cars was terrific. Ernie strained his eyes to follow De Palma with each whirl around the track. The Mercedes was tearing off lap after lap at tremendous speed. Dawson and Tetzlaff kept trading second and third place.

Wild Bob Burman had two blowouts on his 157th lap. His car turned upside down. A groan went up from the crowd. They were sure Wild Bob and his mechanic had been killed. But before the rescue party arrived, both men crawled out. They stood beside their car until it was dragged off, out of the race.

Later, another car went off the track. Its nose came to a stop by a telegraph pole and hung on the wall. The mechanic and driver jumped out unhurt. The crowd cheered. Ernie cheered loudest of all.

Papa soon gave up Gil Anderson, his number-one man, because he was dropping far behind. Terrible Teddy stayed in third place.

Thad yelled for Joe Dawson. "Get up there, Joe! Pass De Palma!"

Ernie beamed. De Palma was still first, several laps ahead.

At last, after many hours, the long, long race was almost over. De Palma had only three more laps to go. When those laps were run, De Palma would win the race!

Suddenly the smooth roar of De Palma's engine changed. His exhaust began coughing. Ernie listened in dismay. Something was wrong.

"His engine is missing!" The anxious cry came from all sides. Ernie groaned.

De Palma's Mercedes slowed down in the back stretch. When it came by the stands, it was crawling. Everyone was on his feet, shouting encouragement. He was still four whole laps ahead of

Dawson. There wouldn't be time now for him to stop at the pits.

He had only two more laps to go. Perhaps his engine would right itself! Instead, he went more and more slowly in the back stretch. Suddenly his car came to a dead stop. Something must have broken. Everyone groaned.

Joe Dawson began streaking around on his last three laps. Thad cheered him on. Ernie was yelling his lungs out for De Palma.

De Palma and his mechanic jumped out. Frantic, they started pushing. They pushed the heavy Mercedes until they reached the pits. There the two men collapsed against the side of the car. What a heartbreaking finish—with only one more lap to go!

Now Dawson whizzed down the homestretch. A roar went up from the stands. The checkered victory flag dropped. Joe Dawson was the winner!

Thad pounded Ernie on the back. Terrible Teddy came in second.

Ernie had eyes for no one but De Palma. The driver looked dead tired, but he dragged himself over to the beaming Dawson. He was the first to shake the winner's hand.

"See what I mean?" Ernie's eyes were shining. "He's the best sport of them all. I'd rather be like De Palma than anybody else in the whole world."

Ernie smiled as he shook hands with Thad. "Congratulations, Thad," he said. "You win—you and Joe Dawson."

Hallowe'en

ONE CHILLY October evening after dark there was a loud knock on the Pyle's back door. Ernie's mother was washing dishes.

"Ernest," she called, "go see who it is."

Ernie did not answer. Where was that boy? Mama dried her hands on her apron and went to the door herself.

A tramp stood on the back porch. He had a battered old hat pulled down over his eyes. His ragged clothes seemed much too large for him. Ernie's mother started to close the door. The tramp put out his foot and held the door open.

"What do you want?" Mama asked sharply.

"Please, ma'am, I'm hungry." The tramp spoke in a high, squeaky voice. "Can't you spare a cup of coffee and a sandwich? A chicken sandwich, ma'am, and a piece of punkin pie?"

"Well, I never!" Mama said. She was indignant. "I'm not serving sandwiches and pie and coffee to strangers, like a restaurant. Be off with you, Mister!"

The tramp turned as if to go. Then, instead, he ducked under Mama's arm. He scuttled right into the kitchen.

"I'm no stranger, ma'am. You ought to remember me," he said. Mama looked sharply at the tramp. Then she began to laugh. She laughed until the tears came into her eyes.

"Ernest Taylor Pyle! You sure had me fooled for a minute! I forgot all about its being Halloweʼen. In that outfit you look every bit as bad as that Willie the Wanderer."

Ernie took off his old hat and bowed just as

Willie the Wanderer had bowed to him, years ago. "Suppose I can fool Mariam, too?"

"Maybe you'll fool her too well. She probably won't even let you into her Hallowe'en party, you look so raggedy."

Ernie looked hopeful. "Do you suppose there's a chance of that? Then Thad and I could skip the party. The girls are the only ones who want to go. The boys don't. We'd rather go around to different houses and see what we can get to eat."

"Now, Ernest, of course Mariam will let you in. I was just teasing. When she invited the seventh grade, all twelve of you accepted, didn't you? It's too late to back out now. It would hurt her feelings if you and Thad didn't show up. Besides, I thought you liked Mariam."

"Oh, I like her all right. She's the best girl in the class. But we've got only four boys in our room, and parties with a bunch of girls aren't much fun."

"Well, this party sounds nice," Mama went on. "Her mother tells me Mariam has gone to a lot of trouble. She has worked hard on her costume and on the refreshments. She has planned some good games for all of you, too. Maybe this will be different from the parties where you have to get all dressed up in your Sunday clothes with nothing to do."

Mama laughed again as she looked at Ernie. "And you certainly don't have on your Sunday clothes tonight. I never saw such an outfit! I thought I'd thrown away those old things of Papa's long ago."

Ernie grinned. "I fished them out of the trash pile. There! I hear Thad's whistle. I've got to go now, I guess."

Ernie rolled up the ragged sleeves of the coat, which was much too large for him. He pulled the battered old hat down over his eyes and dashed out the back door.

In the yard Ernie stopped in surprise. Thad was nowhere to be seen. Ernie whistled. There was no answer. There was no sound except the crackling of dry leaves in the wind.

The moon was just rising. It looked like a huge ripe orange. In its yellow light the trees made long, black shadows.

Ernie peered all about him. What was that in the grape arbor? Something white was silently swaying back and forth. Ernie caught his breath. Was it—could it be a ghost? Then Ernie knew. He laughed.

"Come out of there, you old ghost!" he called. "You can't scare a tramp like me."

Thad's muffled laugh came from the ghostly figure. "For a minute there I had you scared. You should have seen the look on your face. Darn this sheet! I keep tripping on it."

Thad came out, clutching at the sheet. It kept

getting in his way. All Ernie could see of Thad were his two eyes. They looked out brightly through the slits in an old pillowcase.

Together the boys started across fields toward Mariam's house. Thad had a hard time climbing over fences.

"Why don't you just float over them?" Ernie teased. "That's what any real honest-to-goodness ghost would do."

"I wish I could," Thad said. "Next Hallowe'en I'm not going to be a ghost. Ghost clothes are too flappy."

"Well, anyhow, you won't have to talk much at the party," Ernie consoled him. "Ghosts hardly ever talk."

"Oh, this ghost is different," Thad said cheerfully. "I can talk all right, even when I have a pillowcase over my head."

Ernie looked at Thad enviously. "That's the truth," he thought. "Thad never gets tongue-tied the way I do. Not even when girls are around. I'm the one who ought to be wearing a pillowcase. Then I'd have a good excuse not to talk when I can't think what to say."

Now the Baleses' house loomed up in front of the boys in the moonlight. On the porch a huge carved pumpkin smiled a toothy welcome. Inside the pumpkin a candle flame wavered in the breeze.

Ernie grabbed Thad's arm. "Let's see if anybody else is there before we go in," he whispered. "We don't want to be the first ones."

THE GIRLS IN THE PARLOR

Stealthily the boys crept up beside the porch to the house. They looked through the brightly lighted window. They saw several gaily dressed figures sitting around the parlor.

"There're lots of people here already," whispered Thad. "See that old witch? Wonder who that is? And look at that big rag doll. She sure is a limp one! And boy, look at that pretty Dutch girl! Come on, if we have to go in, we might as well go now."

"No, wait a minute," Ernie whispered. "Let's see who they are, first. Mariam is the Dutch girl —I can tell by her long braids. But I can't tell who that is dressed up like Bopeep. Or any of the others, with all those masks on. But, gee, they're all girls! The other two guys haven't come yet. Let's wait for them. We don't want to be the only fellows."

Thad and Ernie got the giggles as they watched the girls who sat primly on the chairs in the Baleses' parlor. They all looked as though they were waiting for something to happen.

"Waiting for us, most likely," Thad whispered. "They don't want to start the party till the boys come."

"Girls are sure funny," Ernie said. "You'd think they could have a party without us. They look awfully stiff and solemn. I wish we didn't have to go in at all. We could have a heap more fun by ourselves, tearing around."

Suddenly Thad grabbed Ernie. "Look out! Duck! Mariam saw us!"

As they ducked, they heard Mariam scream. "Look! A ghost! And a tramp! Looking in through the window!"

As the boys crouched out of sight below the sill, they heard the girls all rush to the window. An excited chattering broke out.

"Where?"

"I don't see any ghost."

"No tramp, either."

"Are you sure you saw someone?"

Then the boys heard Mariam's voice again. "Cross my heart, I did. The whitest ghost you ever saw! And a ragged old tramp!"

"Weren't you scared?" came another voice.

Mariam laughed. "For a minute I was, but it's probably just the boys. Come on, everybody. Let's go outside and see."

Ernie and Thad did not waste a minute. They dashed across the yard, away from the house.

"Quick! We can hide behind the hedge!"

Ernie got there first. Thad tripped once on his sheet. But they were both safe behind the hedge when the girls trooped out on the porch.

The boys smothered their laughter as they watched. The girls ran along the porch, peering in all directions. Mariam came boldly down the steps and into the yard, looking around her. The boys could see her white Dutch cap bobbing in the moonlight.

"Oh, you just made it up, Mariam!" the Rag Doll called from the porch. "There isn't anybody out here."

Mariam tossed back her long braids. "I didn't

either make it up. If it's the boys, they're hiding. I'm not going to hunt for them."

Bopeep laughed. "'Leave them alone and they'll come home, wagging their tails behind them," she said.

Mariam said, "Yes, let's go in. It's time to start the party, boys or no boys." She sounded disappointed, but she turned and went into the house with the other girls.

The front door closed. In the parlor someone pulled down the window blind.

THE PARTY

Thad got up from his knees. Ernie helped him brush leaves from his sheet. He said, "One good thing about a tramp's outfit: you never have to brush anything. Dirt and leaves just make it look better."

He looked at Thad. "I reckon we'd better not

wait any longer for the other guys. Hey, that must be the fellows now!"

Two strange figures were turning in at the gate. A scarecrow and an Indian stalked up to Ernie and Thad. "Say, we went over to both your houses, looking for you," the Indian said. "You don't want to go to this old party, do you?"

The scarecrow waved his arms stiffly. "Come on with us. We're going to go to everybody's house and do all kinds of things. Maybe we'll get some handouts."

"Gee, we'd like to," Ernie said, "but——" He stopped and looked at Thad, then at the others. "We promised Mariam we'd come to her house. You told her you would, too, didn't you?"

"Yes, but we've changed our minds," the Indian said. "I've got a ticktack. We can make a racket with it on people's windows. Come on."

Thad spoke up. "What do you say, Ernie? Let's skip the party. I will if you will."

Ernie hesitated. Ticktacking on windows and fooling people sounded tempting. "But, golly," he thought, "Mariam's gone to a lot of trouble! And I promised."

He made up his mind. "I guess I'll stay here," he said. He looked at Thad anxiously. What if Thad deserted him now! "You can go if you want to, Thad."

"I'll stay if you stay," Thad said. "Maybe we can leave early. If we do, we'll look for you guys then."

Ernie was pleased. "Good old Thad. He always sticks with me," he thought.

A minute later, when Mariam answered the door, a tramp shuffled in. Beside him glided a ghost. Just as they entered the parlor full of girls, the ghost tripped and fell sprawling.

The party was not a bit stiff after that. Ernie and Thad had such a good time they forgot all about leaving early.

Later that night, on the way home, Ernie said, "Mariam had some good ideas for her party. I thought I'd split when Bopeep was blindfolded and I popped those skinned grapes into her mouth. Did you hear her yell when I told her they were cats' eyes she was eating!"

Thad laughed. "Yes, and that cold spaghetti I fed Rag Doll! She more than half believed me when I told her they were worms! Girls may be silly, but they're kind of fun," he added. "It was a good party."

Ernie agreed. "More fun than just tearing around. But I don't think Mariam's silly. She knows the kind of party boys like. She said she was glad we came. I'm glad we stayed."

Two New Caps

"Why don't you eat your supper, Ernest?" Mama asked.

"My throat hurts," Ernie said.

Mama gave him a quick look. "You do sound a little hoarse. Have you been yelling too much again? Remember when you came back from the 500-mile race last year? You were hoarse for a week."

Ernie pushed his plate away. "No, I haven't been yelling. My throat just burns. Every time I swallow, it hurts."

"Come here and stick out your tongue. Let me see."

Obediently Ernie stuck out his tongue. His mother tilted his head back. She took a long look at his throat. "I think you'd better go to bed. Right now."

"Oh, I can't! I have homework to do. I have to write a composition."

Mama was firm. "You don't have to do any such thing. Not with a throat like that. Now then, off to bed with you! I'm going to call the doctor right away."

Ernie tried to protest, but he felt so miserable that he gave in.

The next day a sign went up on the door. It read QUARANTINE—DIPTHERIA.

Ernie was in bed for several weeks. Old Shep stayed most of the time right outside the door to Ernie's bedroom.

"I declare I never saw such a faithful dog," Mama told Ernie. "He feels as bad as all the rest of us do about you being sick."

At last Ernie's throat began to clear up, and he could swallow again. One evening Mama hummed a little tune as she carried his tray out to the kitchen.

"There, just look at that," she said to Papa. "Tonight for the first time he drank every drop of his milk through the straw. He even wants me to play some music for him."

Ernie dozed off. When he woke up an hour later, he heard soft music. Mama was in the parlor, playing her violin. She was playing one of the songs he liked best. It was "On the Banks of the Wabash."

Ernie smiled as he listened to his mother play. As the music drifted in to him, he thought of the words to the song:

Oh, the moonlight's fair tonight along the
  Wabash,
From the fields there comes the breath of new-
  mown hay,

Thro' the sycamores the candle lights are
gleaming,
On the banks of the Wabash, far away.

"The Wabash River isn't so far away," he thought contentedly. "Just down the road a few miles. Soon I'll be going fishing there again. Right across the fields out there is the schoolhouse. I'll be out of bed and back in the seventh grade in no time. I'm getting well again."

Within a few weeks Ernie was well and ready to go back to school.

"You've got to be careful, though, Ernest," Mama said with an anxious look. "Sometimes I'm afraid you never will be as sturdy as you ought to be."

"Oh, pooh, I feel fine! The only thing is my voice. It sounds funny—kind of squeaky. That's why I clear my throat so often. When I do that, my voice sounds deeper, more the way it should."

Thad and Ernie's other friends did not care how his voice sounded. They were delighted to have him back in school.

"It's a lot better around here, now you're back," one of the boys said. "Nobody else has such good ideas."

Ernie's classmates all agreed. "Now we can have some fun at lunch hour," they said.

Mariam spoke up. "Even English class isn't so bad now. That composition you wrote today on horses was good—about how you like horses for fun, but how you hate them for work."

Thad laughed. "I liked the end, too, where you told how tired you get of plowing behind the south end of a horse going north." Then he added, "I reckon all of us boys feel the same way, but darn it, we never thought to write about it."

Ernie glowed. "We have a good bunch of kids in our class," he said. "If we just stick together, we'll have a fine time next year in the eighth grade and all through high school."

GRADUATION

Ernie's class, the class of 1918, did stick together until they were seniors in high school. By that time the United States was at war with Germany, and Thad left school to join the army.

Ernie was determined to go, too. He grew more and more unhappy. At home he argued with his family.

"What's the use of homework at a time like this! What's the use of school! I've just got to go! Whether I get in the Army or the Navy I don't care. They need volunteers. You know they do!"

"Now, Ernest," his father said. "We've talked this over before. All we ask is that you finish high school. Farm work is important, too, don't forget. Food is scarce—you are helping to raise it. Farm labor is scarce—I need your help. You're doing something for the war just by working in the fields after school."

Mama looked troubled. "Maybe you will have to go to war sometime, Ernest, but finish school first. Then you can apply for a commission and be an officer."

"Officer! Who cares about being an officer!" Ernie answered. "Its privates, doughboys, the Army needs. If it weren't for them, there wouldn't be an Army!"

In the end, Papa put his foot down. "You can't enlist until after graduation at least," he said finally. "That's all there is to it, Ernest. Then we'll see."

Ernie found it hard to study that spring. He hated the plowing more than ever. He was anxious for commencement to come, just to get it over with.

He had no interest in the plans his classmates were making. "What does it matter who gives a speech on graduation night?" he thought. "I'm just glad I don't have to. Who cares what the invitations are like—whether or not we have a gold and purple tassel on them?

"And who gives a darn where we'll print the class motto on the program: 'Climb, though the rocks be rugged!' Thad is the only one of us who has it rugged these days. Off there in an Army camp, about to be shipped overseas to fight in the trenches against the Germans!"

A week before commencement Ernie had an idea. There was one thing, after all, he did care about. He talked it over with his classmates. They liked his idea. They decided that Ernie and Mariam should talk to the principal about it.

In the principal's office Ernie cleared his throat and spoke up. "Thad is still a member of our class, even if he is off in the Army. We want to have his chair up there on the platform with us at graduation."

"An empty chair?" the principal asked in surprise. "Why?"

"When people look at the chair they'll remember Thad," Mariam said quickly.

"Yes, and they'll remember why he isn't here," Ernie added. "We don't want anyone to forget Thad belongs to our class."

"I'll think it over," the principal promised.

By the night of graduation, May 3, Ernie did not know how he could get through the commencement exercises. At home he said, "I ought to be off doing what Thad is. I'm so ashamed not to be, that I've a good notion not even to go to graduation."

Still, when he saw how proud and eager his father and mother were, he decided to go. "I ought to do that much for their sake," he thought.

"You're the only one of the family to get a

high-school diploma," Mama said. "This is a big night for the Pyles. Of course you'll go. We're all going. Now hurry and put on your good suit. It's all brushed and ready for you."

The graduation exercises were a blur to Ernie. He was conscious of only one thing: Thad's empty chair. It was beside him on the platform. Across it the principal had draped a large American flag.

At last the ceremonies ended. Ernie gave his diploma to his father and mother. They smiled proudly when they saw his name engraved on the parchment: ERNEST TAYLOR PYLE.

"It was a good program," his mother said, "and you looked nice up there in your Sunday suit."

"I guess the program was all right," Ernie answered. "At least it's over."

Suddenly he felt happier than he had in months. He grinned. "I'll not be wearing my Sunday suit much longer. Instead, I'll be wearing a uniform."

Before the summer was over, Ernie joined the Navy. He was just getting used to his sailor's uniform when the war ended.

Back home again, he complained to his family. "I didn't even get to march up the gangplank of a battleship!" he said.

"Thank goodness for that!" Mama answered. "Now you can go to college."

"It's a good thing I still have my Navy pea jacket," Ernie said. "It will keep me good and warm this winter down at Indiana University. I guess I can't wear my white hat any more, though. It might look strange."

Ernie tossed his white hat up on the closet shelf. "As soon as I get to Bloomington I'll have to get a little green cap. All the new boys wear them at the University. That's so everyone will know they're freshmen."

Ernie grinned. "I'll look like a brand-new freshman, all right, and that isn't all. With that green cap on my red hair, I'll look like Father Christmas himself!"

Shortest Speech on Record

THREE THOUSAND cheering students poured onto Jordan Field on the Indiana University campus. The college band played its liveliest marches. In the light of a huge bonfire the brass horns sparkled. The tip of a baton shone white whenever the band leader tossed his stick high into the air. He caught it every time.

The bonfire flamed higher and higher. It cast a glow on the faces of the crowd. The red hair of one boy blazed like a torch in the light of the fire. Ernie Pyle, college senior, threw back his head and joined in the singing. He sang "Indiana, Our Indiana."

The football team and the coach filed up the steps of a wooden platform. As the song ended, the cheerleader in his crimson sweater stepped forward to the front of the platform.

"You all know why we're here," he said. "We're here to cheer the team on to victory in tomorrow's game."

"Beat Purdue!" The shouts came from all sides. "Beat Purdue!"

"That's just what we're going to do!" the cheerleader cried. "Now let's hear from some of the men who are going to win the Purdue game for Indiana."

One after another, members of the team were presented to the cheering throng. The captain made a speech. The coach made a stirring talk. The crowd cheered again and again. They sang. They whistled.

The cheerleader held up his hand for silence. "There's someone else we want to mention. He's a little guy who never carried a ball on the field. He never tooted a horn in the band. But on the side lines he has worked harder than anyone else to give the team and the band this send-off, the best send-off ever!"

Students looked at one another uncertainly. What little guy was he talking about?

"You all know him," the cheerleader went on. "Who's that skinny redhead who came here as a green freshman three years ago from a farm up near Dana?"

"Ernie Pyle!" several people in the crowd shouted together.

"Who's the boy who is always writing for the campus paper? First he was a reporter. Then he was an editor. Last summer he was editor-in-chief. Who is he?"

"Ernie Pyle!" shouted five hundred voices.

"Who worked his way as bellboy on a ship across the Pacific last spring? He did it just so he could follow our baseball team to Japan and see the world. Who did that?"

A thousand voices yelled "Ernie Pyle!"

The cheer leader went on: "Remember last week when the band hadn't a cent to make the trip to Purdue? Who had the bright idea of organizing an auto-polo game? Who drove a car himself in the show? And who raised more than enough money to send the band off tomorrow in a blaze of glory?"

"Ernie Pyle!" The answer came from three thousand throats.

"And who's the manager of our football team, the first student manager in the history of Indiana University?"

"Ernie Pyle!" the crowd roared.

"We want Ernie! We want Ernie!" Students everywhere took up the chant.

The boys nearest Ernie started pushing him forward. Ernie ducked and tried to escape, but there was no escape. He was pushed and pulled right up onto the platform.

"Speech! Speech!" everyone yelled.

Ernie looked around for help. Below him was a blur of faces. They were friendly faces—he could see that—but knowing they were friendly did not help his stage fright.

In the sudden quiet Ernie cleared his throat. "Tomorrow I'll celebrate Indiana's victory," he began, "but tonight——"

Ernie stopped. "What on earth can I say next?" he wondered. He tried to go on. "But tonight I'm tongue-tied. I guess I was born that way. And so all I can say is——"

"What *can* I say?" he thought desperately. "Maybe a gesture would help." He flung his arm straight out from his side, but his mind went blank. Not another word would come.

There was only one thing to do: get down off the platform fast. He edged over to the steps.

As he started down from the platform, he shook his head helplessly and grinned. "Never could make a speech," he muttered.

The crowd howled with delight, for Ernie's arm was still sticking straight out from his side.

The cheerleader jumped to his feet. "Who gets three cheers for the shortest speech on record?"

"Ernie Pyle! Ernie Pyle! Ernie Pyle!"

The Roving Reporter

After college, in 1923, Ernie went to work as a cub reporter on a newspaper, the *Herald,* in La Porte, Indiana. Soon he moved to the *Daily News* in Washington, D. C. At last he could see the Washington Monument for himself.

For years, however, he was so busy that he had little time for sightseeing. But he always found time for friends, for people. Before long he met and married a girl named Geraldine. Ernie called her Jerry.

One day he rushed home from the newspaper office. He burst through the apartment door. "Jerry! Jerry!" he called excitedly. "I've got it!"

Jerry looked up from the book she was reading. "You've got what? A million dollars?"

Ernie grabbed the book from her hands and danced her around the room. "It's better than a million dollars," he said. "It's a new job, the best job in the world!"

Ernie beamed. "Just think! No more sitting behind a desk! No more sticking to the same old office! No more writing headlines or editing other people's stories! No more——"

Jerry laughed. "Ernie, stop! You're making me dizzy. Now tell me what has happened."

Ernie gave her a final whirl. He took a deep breath. Then he said, "The Scripps-Howard papers are making me their roving reporter. From now on I can go where I please and write what I please. What do you think of that?"

Jerry was delighted. "It's just the kind of thing you've always wanted to do, isn't it? When do we start?"

"*We?*" Ernie teased. "Who said anything about your going along?"

"Of course I'm going," Jerry said. "You're lucky to have a wife who is willing to bounce around the country with you in that old car. Wouldn't it be awful if you had married someone who wanted to stay home and dust furniture?"

Ernie grinned. "Wouldn't it be awful if you had married some old stick-in-the-mud who never took you anywhere? I know! From now on you'll be 'That Girl who rides with me.' So pack your suitcase, Mrs. Ernest Taylor Pyle. It's the gypsy life for us!"

The next week was a busy one. Ernie and Jerry said good-by to all their Washington friends. Early one morning Ernie loaded the old car with his typewriter, a camera, dozens of books, and two suitcases.

"After all," he said, "we won't need many clothes for traveling."

Jerry agreed. "You really ought to get a new hat, though," she said. "The one you have is so old you can't even tell what color it is."

Ernie grinned. "It used to be gray years ago. Then it turned cat-colored. Now it doesn't have any color at all. But I've worn it so long it's part of me now. I can't leave it behind any more than I could leave my typewriter. You never know when a hat like this will come in handy."

"When, for instance?" Jerry asked.

"Well, say we get stuck in the mud somewhere. This hat is just the thing to put under a tire and help pull us out. You couldn't do that with a brand new hat."

Jerry laughed. "Oh, all right. Put it on and wear it, then. Here's the dictionary. We almost forgot it. You never can tell when a dictionary will come in handy, too."

She climbed in the car. "Ready, Ernie?"

"Ready and rarin' to go," Ernie said.

"Where are we going?" Jerry asked.

"Anywhere—everywhere," Ernie said. "I'll just follow my nose and see where it takes us."

For the first few weeks Ernie drove fast. One day Jerry protested. "Slow down, Ernie. You're not on the Speedway in Indianapolis, you know."

Ernie looked at the speedometer and saw that he was going 80 miles an hour. "Whew!" he said as he took his foot off the accelerator. "That's too fast for the likes of us. We aren't going anywhere in particular, and we have all the time in the world to get there!"

After that he took his time. Whenever he found a good story, he stopped for a day or two. He would talk to all kinds of people. Then he would write his story in his hotel room that night.

He wrote about all sorts of things. He wrote about mountain climbing, making soap, and polio. He wrote about digging for gold, zippers that stuck, and his folks back home in Dana.

More and more people began to read his columns in the newspapers. "Reading them is just like getting a letter," they said.

"That's just about what I am," Ernie said, "a letter writer."

One day when they were out West Ernie said, "There's a place I've always wanted to see. It's called Four Corners, and it's not far away. It's the only place in the United States where four states come together."

Jerry counted them off on her fingers. "Colorado, Utah, Arizona—and what else?"

"New Mexico, of course," Ernie said. "If we ever stop wandering, let's build ourselves a house in New Mexico. I like the state. Today, though, we'll just have a look at Four Corners."

It was a long bumpy ride to Four Corners. First there was a dirt road, then a rocky, sandy uphill track. Once Ernie had to use the old hat to stop the back wheel from spinning in the sand.

Finally they reached Four Corners. They found nothing there but a concrete post and two swallows that kept flying around. The post, put up by the government, was about two feet high. A bronze marker on top of it had two short lines crossed in the middle to show the boundary lines of the four states.

Ernie sat on top of the post. "Not everybody can sit in four states at once," he said.

Jerry got out of the car with her camera. "Hold still and I'll take your picture," she said.

Then she brought out a picnic lunch. Ernie sat on the post to eat his. While they ate, he and Jerry counted up the states they had been in since they left Washington months before.

"All forty-eight," Ernie said finally, "and Alaska. Someday we'll go to Hawaii, too. But let's start back to the hotel now. I want to write about eating peanut butter and jelly sandwiches in four states at once."

Things weren't always funny or easy for Ernie. Sometimes he grew discouraged. Sometimes he or Jerry was sick. Often his work was hard work. But it was the kind of work that Ernie liked best —travel and writing.

Whenever he could, Ernie stopped off in Indiana to see his family. One time, driving along on the way home, Ernie said, "Remember that farmer back in Kansas who had six life-size statues made so people would remember him?

"Well, maybe I'd better have six statues made of me. I'd stand them up across Highway 36 near Dana. People would bump smack into them. Then they wouldn't forget me."

Jerry laughed. "People might remember you more kindly if there were just a bronze marker by the side of the road with your name on it."

"I'd settle for that," Ernie said. "But markers aren't put up to people who are afraid of snakes and who write columns that are like letters."

On that visit home Ernie's family asked him, "Aren't you getting awfully tired of traveling around all the time?"

Ernie answered truthfully, "No, not yet. At least it's better than getting up before daylight to milk cows."

It was a good thing that Ernie was not sick of travel. There was much more of it in store for him.

After World War II broke out, Ernie left Jerry, "That Girl," behind in the United States while he went to countries where the fighting was going on. He wore a correspondent's uniform, but he didn't carry a gun. Instead, he carried his typewriter wherever he went.

Always, wherever he went and whatever he saw, the columns he wrote were like letters to millions of anxious people back home.

Ernie's GI's

IN A FOXHOLE in North Africa two soldiers were enjoying a breathing spell. After last night's big battle the area was fairly quiet. The retreating enemy had left behind only one machine gun. It was hidden somewhere on the hill. Once in a while there was a burst of firing. Bullets whined overhead.

"Say," the tall soldier said to the shorter one, "see that guy sitting out there by that rock? He'd better get under cover. Who is that little guy, anyhow? Looks as if he's writing."

"Don't you know who that is?" said the other. "That's Ernie Pyle!"

"The famous Ernie? I should have known that's who it was. He's always turning up in the thick of things. They say the generals keep asking him to stick around headquarters, but he'd rather be with us GI's. Why, my folks have been reading his newspaper column about the war ever since I've been over here."

"Only since then?" the other GI broke in. "My family was reading his stuff long before the war. Why, for years they'd look in the paper for Ernie Pyle's column before they even looked at the weather report. I can still hear my dad laughing at the way Ernie would describe the places and the people he saw and the funny experiences he had."

"Well, I guess he's not having such funny experiences these days. I'd like to go over and talk to him, but he looks too busy."

"He ought to get busy and get away from that rock," said the first GI. "The white paper he's writing on makes a good target for that enemy machine gunner."

"Look out, Ernie!" yelled the tall soldier.

At that moment machine gun bullets spattered all around Ernie like hail.

He looked up. Then he came in a crouching run to the foxhole. As he dropped into its shelter he grinned at the two GI's. "That was kind of close. Too close for comfort. Mind if I stay here for a while?"

"Glad to have you." Both GI's beamed.

"Now we'll have something to write home about!" the tall soldier said. "Wait till we tell them who popped into our foxhole!"

"Say, where's your typewriter?" asked the other soldier. "I thought you always used one."

Ernie laughed. "I do, usually. But this time I left it back in camp. It's bulky when you're up at the front. A pencil's easier. Mind if I get on with the job?"

"Go right ahead."

Ernie sat down and started to write. The two GI's looked over his shoulder. They read the sentences as they came quickly and surely from Ernie's pencil. He was writing about what he had seen the last few nights. He wrote about the long lines of tired, grimy men coming back from the battle.

One GI nudged the other. "Wait till they read this in the home-town paper! My girl seems to have the idea I'm a handsome hero in a spick-and-span uniform. She must think I'm always marching in a dress parade, or something. I don't dare tell her I haven't even washed for a week. But you tell her, Ernie."

Ernie grinned and went on writing.

The machine-gun fire stopped. Other GI's crawled out of their foxholes, came over and peered down at Ernie. He glanced up every now and then to say "Hi!"

When he finished, he folded his paper and stuck it in his pocket. "That's done," he said. "Now all of you tell me your names and home addresses." Ernie jotted them down in his little notebook. "I'll put these in a story later."

"How about giving us your autograph, Ernie?" The soldiers crowded around him. Quickly he signed his name for each one.

"Time I was getting back to camp," he said. "I haven't had much sleep myself, lately. Too much going on."

Just then a long snake crawled out from some grass on one side of the hole. No one saw it slither across the hole, but it brushed against Ernie's foot. He scrambled out of the hole so fast that all the GI's laughed.

"It's just a snake, Ernie, not a bullet. The machine gun's been stopped."

"I don't care," Ernie said. "I'd almost rather be nudged by a bullet than by one of those crit-

US

ters. I never did care much for snakes. So long, you fellows!"

Back in camp behind the lines, Ernie sent his stories off to his editor in Washington, D.C. Then, too tired to undress, he fell on his hard cot. "Feels good after sleeping on the ground all these nights," he thought. In two minutes Ernie was sound asleep.

THE MAILBAG

When he finally woke up, he found that mail had arrived. There was a big sack of it for Ernie.

Eagerly he looked through his piles of letters. Yes, there was one from his wife, Jerry. She told of their little house in New Mexico. "I am working to make the garden bloom for you," she wrote. "When are you coming home?"

There was a letter from Aunt Mary. "I'm getting hundreds of letters from soldiers' families," she had written. "They all ask for my way of canning chicken. They read in one of your stories how much you like it. Now they want to send some to their boys."

Papa wrote, too. "A magazine has sent a crew of photographers out here to Dana. They've been taking pictures of the home place. They're writing a long article about you and putting your picture on the cover. If only your mother were still living! She would be prouder than ever of her Ernest!"

From their farm in Indiana Mariam and her husband had sent a newsy letter.

There was a post card from Thad, too. "When the war is over, how about going fishing with me? Down here in Florida where I live now, there are bigger fish than we ever caught in Mr. Webster's creek."

There were warm personal letters from General Eisenhower and General Bradley.

"Well, what do you know about this one!" Ernie exclaimed. He had found a note marked THE WHITE HOUSE. An aide wrote that President Roosevelt wanted Ernie to know how much he enjoyed Ernie's newspaper columns. The President depended on them for information he could not get in any other way. Wouldn't Ernie call at the White House when he came back to the United States?

Ernie grinned as he read the letter. "I'd like to meet the President," he thought, "but I wouldn't know what to say. I'd be tongue-tied for sure if I went to the White House."

He looked through another big pile of letters. "There must be a hundred letters here from people I never even heard of," he said to himself. "They're nice letters, too. Lots of them say people worry about me because in my pictures I look thin and worn out. I guess I am worn out, at that. I could use a rest."

A cable arrived from his newspaper office. YOUR STORIES TERRIFIC. IN PAPERS ALL OVER COUNTRY. EVERYBODY TALKING ABOUT THEM. BUT HOW ABOUT COMING HOME FOR A REST? HAVEN'T YOU HAD ENOUGH?

END OF THE JOURNEY

Many months later Ernie did go home, but he could not rest.

"I feel I must go out to the Pacific," he said. "The fighting's still going on out there. I don't want to go. I hate war. I'm sick of it, and I'm scared."

"Why do you go, then?" one of his friends asked. "Nobody's making you go."

"I know it," Ernie answered, "but——"

He thought of something his mother had said to him long ago when he was a small boy. He smiled as he remembered. "Even if my stomach gets scared," he said, "I have to make my feet keep going."

Ernie went to the Pacific, and he kept going until he was killed by an enemy sniper's bullet. It happened on the little island of Ie Shima. Ernie's friends, the GI's, put a marker over his grave.

AT THIS SPOT
THE 77TH INFANTRY DIVISION
LOST A BUDDY
ERNIE PYLE
18 April 1945

More About This Book

WHEN ERNIE PYLE LIVED

1900 ERNIE PYLE WAS BORN NEAR DANA, INDIANA, AUGUST 3.

There were forty-five states in the Union.

William McKinley was President.

The population of the country was about 75,994,000.

1906 ERNIE STARTED TO SCHOOL NEAR DANA.

Theodore Roosevelt was President, 1901-1909.

Orville Wright was injured and Lt. Thomas Selfridge was killed in the first airplane accident in America, 1908.

Henry Ford introduced the first Model T Ford, 1908.

Robert Peary discovered the North Pole, 1909.

Woodrow Wilson was President, 1913-1919.

1914–1918 ERNIE ATTENDED HIGH SCHOOL.

The Panama Canal was completed and opened to world traffic, 1914.

The United States entered World War I, 1917.

1919 ERNIE ATTENDED INDIANA UNIVERSITY AND BECAME A NEWSPAPER REPORTER.

World War I ended, November 11, 1918.

Regular radio broadcasts were begun, 1920.

Airplane mail service was begun, 1920.

Women in the United States were given the right to vote, 1920.

Warren G. Harding was President, 1921-1923.

1923 PYLE BECAME A NEWSPAPER MAN IN WASHINGTON, D. C.

Calvin Coolidge was President, 1923-1929.

Charles A. Lindbergh flew a small airplane across the Atlantic Ocean, 1927.

Stock market prices crashed and a severe business depression followed, 1929.

Franklin D. Roosevelt became President, 1933.

1935 PYLE STARTED A COLUMN AS A ROVING CORRESPONDENT.

Regular airplane flights were started across the Atlantic Ocean, 1939.

World War II started, 1939.

The United States entered World War II, 1941.

1945 PYLE WAS KILLED, APRIL 18.

There were forty-eight states in the Union.

Harry S. Truman was President.

The population of the country was about 140,090,000.

DO YOU REMEMBER?

1. Where was Ernie Pyle born and where did he live as a boy?
2. What frightened Ernie one day when he was picking wild roses for his mother?
3. What did Ernie do about the knife which he dropped when he ran?
4. How did Ernie manage to purchase the post card album that he wanted?
5. How did Ernie decide what to call the new dog which he got from Will Bales?
6. What did Ernie and Thad Hooker find in an Indian mound?
7. How did Ernie and Thad help to prepare for Aunt Mary's wedding?
8. How did Ernie and Thad get caught after the wedding ceremony?

9. How did Ernie entertain Willie the Wanderer at the house one morning?
10. What did Ernie do with the recipe which he copied for his great-aunt, Nancy Miller?
11. How did Ernie manage to win a composition contest when he was in the fifth grade?
12. What did Ernie and Thad see at the Five Hundred Mile Race in Indianapolis?
13. How did Ernie manage to fool his mother on Halloween?
14. What serious illness did Ernie suffer while he was growing up?
15. What short speech did Ernie make at Indiana University?
16. How did Ernie Pyle gather stories in foxholes during World War II?
17. Where and how was Ernie Pyle killed?

IT'S FUN TO LOOK UP THESE THINGS

1. What crops are raised on farms in Indiana, where Ernie Pyle grew up?
2. Where is Indiana University located from which Ernie Pyle graduated?

3. What is the 500-mile race in Indianapolis, which Ernie attended as a boy?
4. What is a roving correspondent, such as Ernie became in 1935?
5. What regions of the world did Ernie Pyle cover during World War II?
6. Where is Ie Shima, the spot where Ernie Pyle was killed?

INTERESTING THINGS YOU CAN DO

1. Write a composition about an interesting experience in your life, just as Ernie Pyle wrote about fishing as an interesting experience.
2. Find out what it means to be a reporter or correspondent and report to the class.
3. Look up the battle of Ie Shima and tell why it was especially important to our cause in World War II.
4. Find out on a map where Ie Shima is located and describe its location to the class.
5. Prepare a list of children's books based on World War II, which would be helpful for you and your classmates to read.

OTHER BOOKS YOU MAY ENJOY READING

An Ernie Pyle Album, Lee Miller. William Sloan Associates, Inc.

Brave Men, Ernie Pyle. Grosset.

Early Days of Automobiles, Elizabeth Janeway. Trade Edition, Random House. School Edition, Hale.

First Book of World War II, Louis Snyder. Watts.

Flying Correspondent, Henry Gregor Felsen. Dutton.

Let's Go to a Newspaper, Laura Sootin. Putnam.

INTERESTING WORDS IN THIS BOOK

arbutus (är bū'tŭs) : vine with pink flowers that bloom in the spring

baton (bȧ tôn') : stick with which a band or orchestra leader beats time

bronze (brŏnz) : reddish-brown alloy or mixture of copper and tin

burlap (bûr'lăp) : coarse cloth made of hemp or flax

capital (kăp'ĭ tăl) : city where the government of a country or state is located

catalogue (kăt′ȧ lŏg) : book containing a list of articles for sale, often illustrated

ceremony (sĕr′ė mō′nĭ) : planned program of events that take place, as at a wedding or funeral

commotion (kŏ mō′shŭn) : noisy disturbance

crimson (krĭm′z’n) : deep red

curlicues (kûr′lĭ kūz) : fancy curves

delectable (dė lĕk′tȧ b’l) : delightful

diphtheria (dĭf thēr′ĭ ȧ) : infectious disease of the throat

engraved (ĕn grāv’d′) : cut in stone, metal, or glass for printing purposes

exhaust (ĕg zôst′) : escaping gases from an automobile engine

foxhole (fŏks′hōl′) : shallow hole dug by soldiers for protection

furrows (fŭr′ōz) : long narrow trenches made by a plow

gangplank (găng′plăngk′) : movable bridge-like platform used for boarding or leaving a ship

gingham (gĭng′ăm) : striped or checked cotton cloth used in making dresses

indignant (ĭn dĭg′nănt) : angry because of unjust treatment

lurched (lûrcht) : moved suddenly from side to side

obediently (ō bē′dĭ ĕnt lĭ) : willingly

pagoda (pȧ gō′dȧ) : tower several stories high with curled-up roofs at the sides and on top

parchment (pärch′mĕnt) : skin of a sheep or goat prepared for use as a writing material

pea jacket: heavy waist-length coat worn by sailors

plaid (plăd) : piece of cloth printed or woven in stripes or checks

primly (prĭm′lĭ) : properly

recipe (rĕs′ĭ pē) : directions for preparing some kind of food

shiftless: lazy

sniper (snī pẽr) : soldier who shoots at enemy soldiers from hidden locations

sorghum (sôr′gŭm) : plant containing sweet juice grown for making sirup or feeding animals

stealthily (stĕlth′ĭ lĭ) : slyly

sulky (sŭl′kĭ) : sullen

surrey (sûr′ĭ) : two-seated, four-wheeled carriage

tremendous (trē mĕn′dŭs) : enormous

valise (vȧ lēs′) : traveling bag

Childhood
OF FAMOUS AMERICANS

COLONIAL DAYS

James Oglethorpe, *Parks*
Myles Standish, *Stevenson*
Peter Stuyvesant, *Widdemer*
Pocahontas, *Seymour*
Pontiac, *Peckham*
Squanto, *Stevenson*
Virginia Dare, *Stevenson*
William Bradford, *Smith*
William Penn, *Mason*

STRUGGLE for INDEPENDENCE

Anthony Wayne, *Stevenson*
Ben Franklin, *Stevenson*
Betsy Ross, *Weil*
Dan Morgan, *Bryant*
Ethan Allen, *Winders*
Francis Marion, *Steele*
George Rogers Clark, *Wilkie*
George Washington, *Stevenson*
Israel Putnam, *Stevenson*
John Paul Jones, *Snow*
John Sevier, *Steele*
Martha Washington, *Wagoner*
Molly Pitcher, *Stevenson*
Nathanael Greene, *Peckham*
Nathan Hale, *Stevenson*
Patrick Henry, *Barton*
Paul Revere, *Stevenson*
Tom Jefferson, *Monsell*

EARLY NATIONAL GROWTH

Abigail Adams, *Wagoner*
Alec Hamilton, *Higgins*
Andy Jackson, *Stevenson*
Dan Webster, *Smith*
DeWitt Clinton, *Widdemer*
Dolly Madison, *Monsell*
Elias Howe, *Corcoran*
Eli Whitney, *Snow*
Francis Scott Key, *Stevenson*
Henry Clay, *Monsell*
James Fenimore Cooper, *Winders*
James Monroe, *Widdemer*
John Audubon, *Mason*
John Jacob Astor, *Anderson*
John Marshall, *Monsell*
John Quincy Adams, *Weil*
Lucretia Mott, *Burnett*
Matthew Calbraith Perry, *Scharbach*
Nancy Hanks, *Stevenson*
Noah Webster, *Higgins*
Oliver Hazard Perry, *Long*
Rachael Jackson, *Govan*
Robert Fulton, *Henry*
Samuel Morse, *Snow*
Sequoyah, *Snow*
Stephen Decatur, *Smith*
Stephen Foster, *Higgins*
Washington Irving, *Widdemer*
Zach Taylor, *Wilkie*

WESTWARD MOVEMENT

Buffalo Bill, *Stevenson*
Daniel Boone, *Stevenson*
Davy Crockett, *Parks*
Jed Smith, *Burt*
Jessie Fremont, *Wagoner*
Jim Bowie, *Winders*
Jim Bridger, *Winders*